TRANSITIONING TO ALTERNATIVE PAYMENT MODELS

A GUIDE TO NEXT GENERATION MANAGED CARE CONTRACTING

1st Edition

DORAL JACOBSEN, MBA, FACMPE
NANCI L. ROBERTSON, BSN, MHA

Medical Group Management Association
104 Inverness Terrace East
Englewood, CO 80112-5306
877.275.6462
mgma.org

Library of Congress Cataloging-in-Publication Data
Names: Jacobsen, Doral, author. Robertson, Nanci L., author
MGMA (Association); publisher.
EGZ Publications; production.
Title: Transitioning to Alternative Payment Models
  p. ; cm.
Description: 1st. Englewood, CO : Medical Group Management Association,
 [2016] Includes bibliographical references and index.

MGMA product id 8917/E8917
PRINT ISBN 978-1-56829-490-2
DIGITAL ISBN 978-1-56829-491-9

Subjects: | MESH: Medical Practice, billing & administration | Efficiency, Organizational | Quality Assurance, Health Care--organization & administration
Classification: LCC R728 (print) | LCC R728 (ebook) | NLM WY 125 | DDC
  610.68--dc23

Printed in the United States of America
10 9 8 7 6 5 4 3 2 1

CONTENTS

ACRONYMS V

CHAPTER 1
INTRODUCTION 1

CHAPTER 2
TRIPLE AIM 11

CHAPTER 3
NARROW NETWORKS 15

CHAPTER 4
PATIENT LIABILITY 27

CHAPTER 5
TRANSPARENCY 31

CHAPTER 6
QUALITY METRICS 35

CHAPTER 7
CONNECTING THE DOTS 39

CHAPTER 8
FEE-FOR-SERVICE 43

CHAPTER 9
PAY-FOR-PERFORMANCE 61

CHAPTER 10
BUNDLED PAYMENTS —EPISODE OF CARE 83

CHAPTER 11
SHARED SAVINGS/RISK 101

CHAPTER 12
CAPITATION — GLOBAL PAYMENT 119

CHAPTER 13
SETTING UP TO SUCCEED 147

CHAPTER 14
CONCLUSION 169

ABOUT THE AUTHORS 171

INDEX 173

Acronyms

Table of Acronyms

ACA	The Patient Protection and Affordable Care Act of 2010
ACG®	Adjusted Clinical Groups ®
ACO	Accountable Care Organization
ACS	American College of Surgeons
ADHD	Attention Deficit Hyperactivity Disorder
AHA	American Heart Association
AHRQ	Agency for Healthcare Research and Quality
AMA	American Medical Association
APM	Alternative Payment Model
AQC	BCBS of Massachusett's Alternative Quality Contract
AR	Accounts Receivable
ASA PS	ASA Physical Status Classification System
AWP	Average Wholesale Price
BCBS	Blue Cross/Blue Shield
BPCI	Bundled Payment Care Improvement
CABG	Coronary Artery Bypass Graft
CAC	Cigna's Collaborative Accountable Care Models
CAHPS®	Consumer Assessment of Healthcare Providers and Systems
CDC	Centers for Disease Control and Prevention
CEC	Comprehensive ESRD Care Model
CHIP	Children's Health Insurance Program
CIN	Clinically Integrated Network
CJR	Comprehensive Care for Joint Replacement
CMS	Centers for Medicare and Medicaid Services
COB	Coordination of Benefits
CPC+	Comprehensive Primary Care Plus
CPT®	Current Procedural Terminology
CT	Computerized Tomography
DME	Durable Medical Equipment
DOFR	Division of Financial Responsibility
DRG	Diagnosis-Related Group
EC	Eligible Clinician

Table of Acronyms (cont.)

ED	EMERGENCY DEPARTMENT
EOB	EXPLANATION OF BENEFITS
ER	EMERGENCY ROOM
ESRD	END STAGE RENAL DISEASE
FFS	FEE-FOR-SERVICE
GI	GASTROINTESTINAL
HCC	HIERARCHICAL CONDITION CATEGORY
HCPCS	HEALTHCARE COMMON PROCEDURE CODING SYSTEM
HEDIS	HEALTHCARE EFFECTIVENESS DATA AND INFORMATION SET
HHA	HOME HEALTH AGENCY
HMO	HEALTH MAINTENANCE ORGANIZATION
IBNR	INCURRED BUT NOT REPORTED
IHA	INTEGRATED HEALTHCARE ASSOCIATION
IHI	INSTITUTE FOR HEALTHCARE IMPROVEMENT
IP	INPATIENT
IRF	INPATIENT REHABILITATION FACILITY
LTCH	LONT-TERM CARE HOSPITAL
MA	MEDICARE ADVANTAGE
MACRA	THE MEDICARE ACCESS AND CHIP REAUTHORIZATION ACT (MACRA)
MCO	MANAGED CARE ORGANIZATIONS
MCPI	MEDICAL CONSUMER PRICE INDEX
MIPS	THE MERIT-BASED INCENTIVE PAYMENT SYSTEM
MLR	MEDICAL LOSS RATIO
MP	MALPRACTICE RVU
MRI	MAGNETIC RESONANCE IMAGING
MSSP	MEDICARE SHARED SAVINGS PROGRAM
MU	MEANINGFUL USE
NCQA	NATIONAL COMMITTEE OF QUALITY ASSURANCE
NG ACO	NEXT GENERATION ACO
NQF	NATIONAL QUALITY FORUM
OCM	ONCOLOGY CARE MODEL TWO-SIDED RISK ARRANGEMENT
OIA	OUTCOME INCENTIVE AWARDS

Table of Acronyms (cont.)

OP	OUTPATIENT
P4P	PAYMENT FOR PERFORMANCE
PCMH	PATIENT-CENTERED MEDICAL HOME
PCORI	PATIENT-CENTERED OUTCOMES RESEARCH INSTITUTE
PCP	PRIMARY CARE PHYSICIAN OR PRIMARY CARE PROVIDER
PE	PRACTICE EXPENSE RVU
PFS	MEDICARE PHYSICIAN FEE SCHEDULE ALSO KNOWN AS PART B FEE SCHEDULE
PMPM	PER MEMBER PER MONTH
POS	POINT OF SERVICE
PPO	PREFERRED-PROVIDER ORGANIZATION
PQRS	PHYSICIAN QUALITY REPORTING SYSTEM
QRUR	QUALITY AND RESOURCE USE REPORTS
RBRVS	RESOURCE BASED RELATIVE VALUE SYSTEM
RVU	RELATIVE VALUE UNITS
SGR	SUSTAINABLE GROWTH RATE
SHOP	SMALL BUSINESS HEALTH OPTIONS PROGRAM
SNF	SKILLED NURSING FACILITY
UCR	USUAL, CUSTOMARY AND REASONABLE
URAC	UTILIZATION REVIEW ACCREDITATION COMMISSION
VM	VALUE-BASED PAYMENT MODIFIER
WAC	WHOLESALE ACQUISITION COST
wRVU	WORK RELATIVE VALUE UNIT

We dedicate this book to our families: husbands Tristan and Keith and children Aryelle, Cayden and Ashley.

Your love, support and encouragement were the most critical ingredients in this journey allowing us to devote time and energy to crafting this manuscript.

We wrote this book for the physicians, clinicians and administrators—working in the trenches and caring for patients—who navigate sweeping changes that touch every aspect of the healthcare industry in this country.

Thank you...

Chapter 1

Introduction

The goal of this book is to offer medical practice leadership teams practical guidance on navigating the shift from volume-based to value-based reimbursement methodologies for both commercial and government payers. Medical practices (both independent and affiliated) that understand how their organization can and should position for the future will have a significant advantage over the competition.

Honestly identifying where you are and defining where you want to be begins with developing a clear understanding of market dynamics (national and local), potential arrangements within your local market and applying those factors to your organization's goals. This exercise can ultimately inform your **Value Proposition**, which becomes the cornerstone of your managed care contracting strategy. We begin by examining what underlies our healthcare system.

U.S. healthcare is rapidly transforming, and it is leaving no sector of the industry untouched. Multiple drivers fuel this healthcare transformation, affecting how patient care is delivered and how it is reimbursed. The affordability crises, unsustainability of costs and an aging population (those eligible for Medicare) are primary drivers fueling the need to reform. The United States spends more than twice as much per capita on healthcare than the average developed country, yet the average American is no healthier than the citizens of developed countries spending less, as depicted in the following table (Fig. 1.1[1]).

---

1 "Health at a Glance 2015: OECD Indicators", OECD Publishing, Paris. DOI: http://dx.doi.org/10.1787/health_glance-2015-en

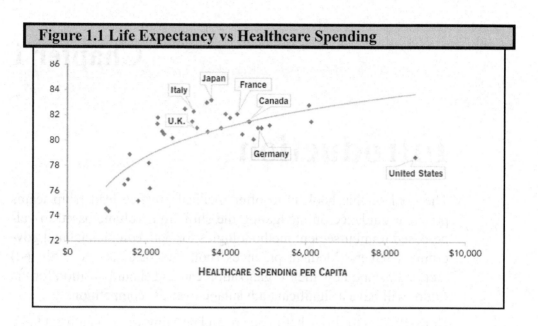

Figure 1.1 Life Expectancy vs Healthcare Spending

The costs far outweigh the benefits. Government projections (see Fig. 1.2[2]) predict healthcare expenditures to be 22% of Gross Domestic Product by 2039. Healthcare expenditures have a stranglehold on the country and the citizens whom the system was developed to help.

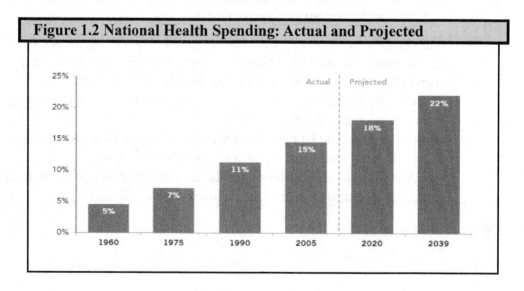

Figure 1.2 National Health Spending: Actual and Projected

---

2 "Analysis: CBO 2014 Long-Term Budget Outlook." Peter G. Peterson Foundation. 2015. Accessed September 20, 2016. http://www.pgpf.org/sites/default/files/sitecore/media%20library/PGPF/Chart-Archive/0056_health-care-costs-proj.pdf

Two key pieces of legislation are driving this transition from volume- to value-based healthcare: The Patient Protection and Affordable Care Act (PPACA, more commonly referred to as "the ACA"), and the Medicare Access and CHIP Reauthorization Act (MACRA). The ACA, signed into law in March 2010, is the most sweeping change in the healthcare system since the creation of Medicare in July 1965. The law encompasses many provisions spanning multiple years. The ACA's primary objectives are aimed at increasing the affordability and rate of health insurance coverage for Americans while reducing overall costs and improving quality of care. It provides a number of mechanisms including innovation models (which can be found at http://innovation.cms.gov/initiatives/), mandates, subsidies and tax credits to employers and individuals to increase the coverage rate and health insurance affordability.

Many innovation models/mechanisms are being explored as the country evaluates their effectiveness in helping transform our healthcare system. The U.S. Department of Health and Human Services set a goal that by the end of 2018, 50 percent of Medicare payments will flow through Alternative Payment Models (APMs) and 90 percent will be tied to quality/value.[3] The implementation of the ACA has accelerated change within the healthcare environment across the country and has redirected the focus of provider payment from volume based to value centered.

MACRA, signed into law in April of 2015, makes significant changes to how Medicare reimburses for services, including:

- Eliminating the flawed sustainable growth rate (SGR) formula previously used to calculate Medicare payments to physicians, resulting in repeated proposals for severe payment cuts,
- Creating a new framework for rewarding healthcare providers for value, and
- Harmonizing current quality reporting systems.

MACRA generally provides a more predictable Medicare payment schedule, directing the Part B payment system towards quality models. Starting in 2019, providers participating in Medicare's Quality Payment Program will enter into one of the following pathways: the Merit-Based Incentive Payment System (MIPS), an Advanced Alternative Payment Model (APM) or a partially qualified APM. The pathway followed will have financial impact (positive or negative) on Medicare payments. This means that not all practices will be paid the same for the care they provide to Medicare beneficiaries. Ultimately, providers could

---

3 Conway, Patrick. "CMS at HIMSS 2015: Day Two Presentations." Health Catalyst CMS at HIMSS 2015 Day Twos Presentations Comments. 2016. Accessed September 20, 2016.

receive between 91 percent to 127 percent (or potentially even more if a scaling factor is applied) of Medicare if they are on the MIPS track or they could receive a 5 percent lump sum bonus annually without downside risk if participating in an Advanced APM (in addition to shared savings/losses through the APM).

By 2026, providers in Advanced APMs will receive 0.5 percent more on their Medicare Physician Fee Schedule than their MIPS counterparts. Advanced APMs will require Medicare revenue thresholds (2019-2020 is 25 percent) or patient thresholds to qualify for classification and, by 2021, the threshold may incorporate commercial payer thresholds. Early adopters who start exploring these value-based models will be positioned for participation in Advanced APMs as commercial APM revenue/patients may count towards the APM threshold starting in 2021.

Advanced APM's for the first performance period in the Quality Payment Program include the following:

- Comprehensive Primary Care Plus (CPC+)
- Medicare Shared Savings Program (MSSP) Tracks 2 and 3
- Next Generation ACO
- Oncology Care Model Two-Sided Risk Arrangement (OCM - available 2018)
- Comprehensive ESRD Care (CEC) Model[4]
- CJR and Cardiac Demonstration (risk dependent)

In these models, providers take on more than nominal financial risk. These Advanced APM models will qualify practices for various incentives, but this is just the start and we expect that there will be additions to this list for models that are at this time undefined. This book explores all types of APM model foundational premises (commercial and Medicare), sharing important considerations that can help you evaluate what will work for your practice. An unprecedented amount of risk lies ahead for physician practices, which is a total game changer, driving transformation across the entire healthcare ecosystem. Only time will tell if the ACA's and MACRA's objectives will be achieved and to what degree, but clearly reimbursement incentives are driving the transformation of how healthcare is delivered.[5,6]

4 "MACRA: Delivery System Reform, Medicare Payment Reform." Accessed September 20, 2016. https://www.cms.gov/Medicare/Quality-Initiatives-Patient-Assessment-Instruments/Value-Based-Programs/MACRA-MIPS-and-APMs/MACRA-MIPS-and-APMs.html.

5 "Quality Payment Program." Accessed September 21, 2016. https://www.cms.gov/Medicare/Quality-Initiatives-Patient-Assessment-Instruments/Value-Based-Programs/MACRA-MIPS-and-APMs/Quality-Payment-Program-MACRA-NPRM-slides-short-version.pdf

6 "MACRA Slide Deck: Educate Your Practice on the Future of Medicare Payment." Accessed September 20, 2016. http://www.mgma.com/government-affairs/washington-connection/2016/april/macra-slide-deck-educate-your-practice-on-the-future-of-medicare-payment.

Figure 1.3 Medicare Payments Under MACRA

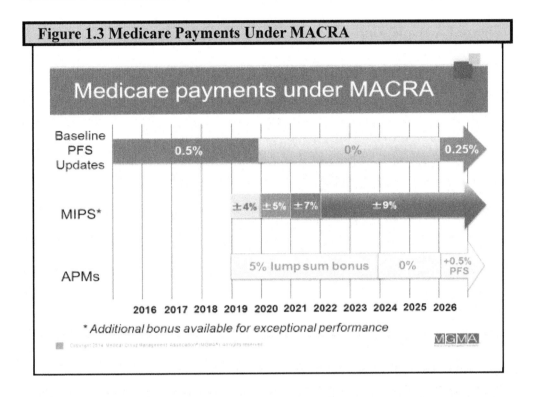

The current payment system, based on sickness and volume, where reactive management is commonplace and more is better, is shifting toward health and wellness, and from **"fee-for-service"** to **"fee-for-value"**. These fee-for-value models represent an evolution in clinical and payment methodologies that focus on creating quality outcomes, fostering greater accountability and employing substantial medical technology innovations requiring a higher degree of risk from providers relative to payment for services. These models contrast starkly with the current system of paying providers based on volume of services provided, regardless of quality and efficiency. These new models intend to align incentives across providers, members, employers and payers to improve clinical outcomes and the patient experience, along with improving cost efficiency, potentially achieving the Institute for Healthcare Improvement's **Triple Aim**. (Fig.1.4)[7]

---

7 "MACRA Slide Deck: Educate Your Practice on the Future of Medicare Payment." Accessed September 20, 2016. http://www.mgma.com/government-affairs/washington-connection/2016/april/macra-slide-deck-educate-your-practice-on-the-future-of-medicare-payment.

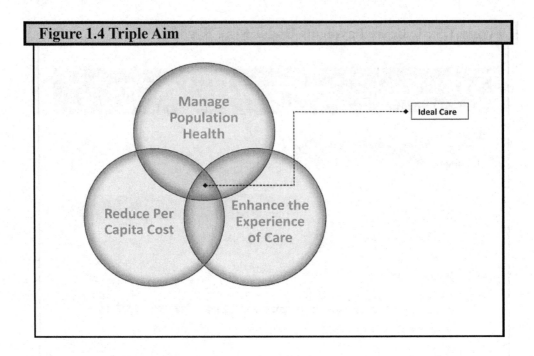

Figure 1.4 Triple Aim

Value is quickly becoming the primary driver as government, as well as commercial payers, experiment with various new value-based reimbursement models (APMs). This process will not occur overnight, but will evolve over time, though it is being accelerated by MACRA as practices must before long decide between MIPS and APMs. Practices will also be challenged by operating in both fee-for-service and fee-for-value environments simultaneously. Practices that thrive in the transformed economic landscape will require skills and tools to evaluate various value-based reimbursements models and participation agreements. Additionally, succeeding in this environment will require a new way of thinking in terms of collaborating with partners such as: payers, facilities, technology vendors, Accountable Care Organizations (ACOs), other providers and more.

These new models emerging in markets across the United States are setting the stage for a more integrated approach to provider/payer relationships. They require deeper collaboration between providers and payers, as elevated levels of data sharing and operations management cooperation will be necessary for high-quality and cost-effective outcomes. This book will explore the payer themes which tie together the common threads of emerging value-based or alternative contracting models found in the commercial and government realms. We will discuss how these trends, vehicles and methodologies interface in order to provide a foundational layer for navigating the different payment models.

We will then turn our focus to describing the various contracting models, beginning with the current prevalent volume-based models, and moving to value-based variants, including:

- Fee-for-Service
- Payment for Performance (P4P)
- Bundled Payments
- Shared Savings/Risk
- Capitation/Global Payment

Figure 1.5 Managed Care Contracting Continuum

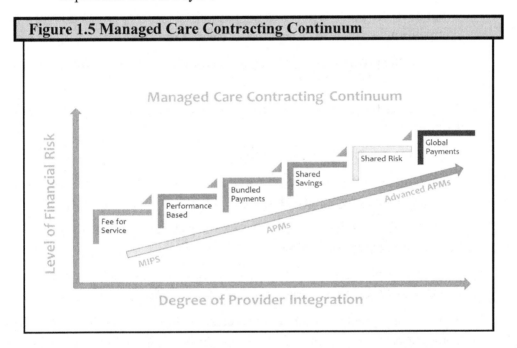

The Managed Care Contracting Continuum (Fig. 1.5) illustrates that the degree of clinical integration correlates to the degree of contract complexity. The more complex the contract, the greater need for clinical integration.

The approach in terms of defining and examining these models will include the following:

- Definition of key attributes,
- Explanations of fundamental drivers,
- Review of negotiation considerations, and

- Examples of financial scenarios.

As these models are unpacked, each practice can consider how it could fit these models into its structure, and begin to identify opportunities for expanding into new contracting territory.

The book's final section is devoted to setting the practice up to succeed. Specifically, how to develop a Value Proposition, including outlining the necessary steps and components of this critical negotiation tool. Understanding the possible models will enable the practice to determine how to answer these essential questions:

- What does the practice offer in the market that differentiates it from the competition?

- Where is the practice in terms of demonstrating how it is working toward achieving the Triple Aim?

- Where does the practice want to be on the Managed Care Contracting Continuum?

- How is the practice going to get there?

- What models is the practice prepared to explore and/or what is the practice open to investigating? MIPS? APM?

- How does the practice garner necessary internal support from the group—specifically group providers?

- Who would be the best partners for the practice (i.e., payers, facilities, groups, ACO, Clinically Integrated Networks [CINs] etc.)?

- What are the greatest potential obstacles and how will the practice overcome them?

- What investment is required in terms of skill sets and tools?

- What is the best way to clearly articulate the practice's Value Proposition?

Once the questions above have been considered, the development of a managed care contracting strategy can be initiated. In this last segment we define the attributes of a successful managed care contracting strategy, including how to develop, deploy and monitor the strategy. The objective is to provide the practice with the necessary foundation, steps and guidelines to position it to succeed in the nation's future healthcare ecosystem.

Anaïs Nin once said: "Life shrinks or expands in proportion to one's courage," so if you are ready explore new territory—and embrace your full practice potential relative to this topic—read on.

Chapter 2

Triple Aim

Payer Common Themes

We begin by discussing common payer themes, which includes the following topics: Triple Aim, narrow networks, patient liability, transparency and quality metrics. The number of acronyms used within the healthcare industry is almost overwhelming, and the nuances of each payer's approach on their value-based contracting transformational programs can add to the confusion. Our goal is to break these down into common threads, laying a foundation for discussing various payment models. Understand that at the core, value-based contracting is about aligning incentives with the goal of creating relationships that will reward the practice for strengthening care coordination, improving health outcomes, lowering costs and providing a better patient experience.

Triple Aim

In October 2007 the Institute for Healthcare Improvement (IHI), a think tank founded by Donald Berwick, MD in Cambridge, Massachusetts, launched the concept of the **Triple Aim**. The Triple Aim goals permeated the Center for Medicare and Medicaid Services (CMS) during Dr. Berwick's tenure as its administrator. Berwick's tenure ended at CMS in 2011, however the creation and development of the Triple Aim will be part of his legacy for years to come. Crafted to be a solution to the healthcare systems ills, the Triple Aim pursues three objectives:

* Improving the experience of care,

* Improving the health of populations, and

* Reducing per capita costs of health care.[1]

Commonwealth Fund explained the significance of the Triple Aim:

---

1 "The IHI Triple Aim." The IHI Triple Aim. Accessed September 21, 2016. http://www.ihi. org/engage/initiatives/tripleaim/pages/default.aspx.

> Pursuing these three objectives at once allows healthcare organizations to identify and fix problems such as poor coordination of care and overuse of medical services. It also helps them focus attention on and redirect resources to activities that have the greatest impact on health. Without balanced attention to these three overarching aims, healthcare organizations may increase quality at the expense of costs, or vice versa. Alternatively, they may decrease cost while creating a dissatisfying experience for patients.[2]

Commercial and government payers alike weave Triple Aim concepts into their programs. Many payers cite integrators, such as Accountable Care Organizations (ACOs), as the primary vehicle for making progress toward achieving the Triple Aim. While Medicare initially led the growth in Medicare Shared Savings Program (MSSP) ACOs starting with the thirty-two Pioneer ACOs in 2011, more than half of the accountable care agreements now come from the private sector.[3]

> The health reform law and subsequent regulations establish a framework where provider groups agree to care for a population of patients with the goal of reaching or surpassing predetermined cost and quality benchmarks. If the ACO manages to meet all the quality benchmarks and the population's cost of care is below the established threshold, the ACO is able to share in the 'savings' (the difference between the actual cost and benchmark cost).[4]

Subsequently, these organizations are designed to align internally to meet and hopefully exceed these targets, taking steps toward achieving the Triple Aim. Considering this realignment in contrast to addressing acute patient needs, ACOs should theoretically act differently, assigning much more value and many more resources to monitoring and intercepting early signs of potential health issues.

While Medicare, Medicaid and commercial programs can vary in terminology, many of the core elements are similar, with the overall strategy being squarely focused the Triple Aim's precepts. Different entities tend to assign their ACOs different names. For example, some entities refer to these structures as Clinically Integrated Networks (CINs). Cigna calls theirs the Collaborative Accountable Care (CAC) models. Blue Cross/Blue Shield (BCBS) of Massachusetts Alternative Quality Contract (AQC) for their HMO product also has attributes of an ACO.[5] The key is to identify the organization's goal. If their mission is to fortify

---

2 "The Triple Aim Journey: Improving Population Health and Patients' Experience of Care, While Reducing Costs." The Commonwealth Fund. Accessed September 21, 2016. http://www.commonwealthfund. org/publications/case-studies/2010/jul/triple-aim-improving-population-health.

3 David Muhlestein. "Continued Growth Of Public And Private Accountable Care Organizations." Health Affairs. N.p., 19 Feb. 2013. Accessed October 07, 2016. http://healthaffairs.org/blog/2013/02/19/continued-growth-of-public-and-private-accountable-care-organizations/

4 ibid.

5 "Alternative Quality Contract." - Visitor. Accessed September 21, 2016. https://www.bluecrossma.com/visitor/about-us/affordability-quality/aqc.html

care coordination, lower healthcare costs and provide a better patient experience, then it is functionally an ACO.

Currently, the majority of ACOs are physician-led, but hospital-led ACOs may actually manage more "lives."[6] One stark contrast between physician-led ACOs and hospital-led ACOS is how they try to achieve savings and manage patient populations. Physician-led ACOs tend to focus on cost efficiency by keeping a patient out of the hospital. They accomplish this by managing patient care in outpatient settings, such as by using patient-centered medical homes to coordinate care among providers, and by utilizing ambulatory surgery centers instead of a hospital setting for procedures. Many hospital-led ACOs focus on improved management of patients once they have been admitted to a hospital by trying to coordinate care among departments and providers. Both approaches encourage appropriate providers, working collaboratively, to treat the patient and more effectively monitor their patient population.

ACOs and their look-a-likes are still a work-in-process, and their success or failure is still to be determined, but ACO's influence on the U.S. healthcare system is already being felt and is an important element to consider for medical practices in terms of contracting strategy.

Suffice it to say, programs across the major private and governmental payers will absolutely include the Triple Aim as a core foundation. They vary in terms of program design, reward system, quality metrics and other attributes, but the essential elements are consistent. The question now is: how will we know if we get there? Donald M. Berwick, Thomas W. Nolan and John Whittington have proposed a "Triple Aim Test," to answer this question.

> Our test has only three items. First, hospitals involved in the Triple Aim would be trying to be emptier, not fuller. They would celebrate as success that the hospital is less and less often needed by the population. Second, the dynamics of supply-driven care would no longer be strong and that patients pull resources, rather than vice versa. And third, patients would say of those who try to maintain and restore their health: "They remember me." They would recognize that the health care system is mindful of their needs, wants, and opportunities for health even when they themselves forget. Health care would also be mindful that people have excellent uses for their wealth other than paying for care they do not need or for illnesses they could have avoided.[7]

---

6 "Continued Growth Of Public And Private Accountable Care Organizations." Health Affairs. Accessed September 21, 2016. http://healthaffairs.org/blog/2013/02/19/continued-growth-of-public-and-private-accountable-care-organizations/

7 Berwick, Donald M., and Thomas W. Nolan And."The Triple Aim: Care, Health, And Cost. 2008". Accessed September 21, 2016. http://content.healthaffairs.org/content/27/3/759

Chapter 3

Narrow Networks

Narrow networks created by payers are comprised of a select panel of providers in response to their customers seeking high-value healthcare at a low cost. By steering patients through these narrow networks, payers expect certain benefits: cost-efficient care, successful adherence to quality metrics and high patient satisfaction. All of these excellent outcomes contribute to payer success; results such as these are expected to drive down expense, which impacts premiums. Narrow networks are not a new phenomenon to the healthcare industry. In the late 1980s, Narrow networks were defined as Preferred Provider Organizations (PPOs) and Health Maintenance Organizations (HMOs).[1] Payers developed select provider networks with the intent to reduce cost and deliver quality, however cost was the primary determining factor: lower reimbursement per unit of service.

Early on, payers instituted a number of programs that were directed to contain cost: select provider networks to include professional, ancillary, and hospital-based facility services, robust utilization management programs requiring primary care to specialty referrals, preauthorization for advanced imaging such as computerized tomography (CT) and magnetic resonance imaging (MRI) scans and for elective surgical procedures. Case management programs were directed to decrease length of stay in inpatient facilities.

Initially, the cornerstone of the quality programs was provider credentialing functions and the submission of Healthcare Effectiveness Data and Information Set (HEDIS). Credentialing functions were often limited to the collection of paper documents with minimal primary source

---

1 Pawlak,Vanessa and Matthew Fadel "Narrow Networks Help Create Value in a More Regulated Healthcare Landscape." Accessed September 21, 2016. http://www.beckershospital-review.com/hospital-management-administration/narrow-networks-help-create-value-in-a-more-regulated-healthcare-landscape.html

verification of actual credentials. Often payers accepted and relied on the credentialing functions performed by their contracted participating hospitals. The majority of providers had limited knowledge and understanding of what HEDIS was and how the care they provided impacted payer results. HEDIS scores are used in ranking health plans and therefore became an important component of payer quality programs.

In the early 1990s, health care accreditation organizations, like the National Committee of Quality Assurance (NCQA) and Utilization Review Accreditation Commission (URAC), came into play. These and other accreditation entities required payers to formalize many of their established processes, policies and procedures with the intent to continuously improve quality. Additionally, employers and the public were provided a means to compare managed care organizations via managed care report cards. Many employers equated successful accreditation achievement to the Good Housekeeping Seal of Approval.

These select narrow networks fell out of favor in the late 1990s. Employers and patients wanted increased access to provider choice, while providers vehemently complained of the added administrative burden taxing their practice. The market responded—payers created new products offering open access at the point of service. The out-of-network concept initially introduced for PPO products was expanded to include HMO products.

In today's healthcare environment, a plethora of names exist to describe present narrow provider network equivalents;

- Clinically Integrated
- High Performance
- High Value
- Employer Specific
- Tailored
- Tiered
- Sub Network

To further complicate matters, payers often create their own unique (or not so unique) definitions for these networks.

So, what went wrong? Annually, healthcare premiums continued to escalate—double-digit increases were not uncommon. Narrow provider networks were presumably designed to contain cost and deliver quality. So if neither objective was ultimately achieved, why is there a proliferation and resurgence of narrow networks? What is different now than in the late 1990s?

Figure 3.1 Network Definitions	
Network Name	**Distinguishing Characteristics**
Clinically Integrated	Network of providers collaborating to improve and maintain the health of a given population
High Performance	Providers deemed to demonstrate high performance on cost efficiency and quality measures
High Value	Providers deemed to demonstrate strong performance in areas of cost efficiency and quality
Employer/Client Specific	Network created by and for a specific employer/client group
Tailored/Narrow/Sub Network	Generally, a subset of the larger provider network
Tiered	Network providers are assigned a tier based on cost efficiency and quality measures. For example, patient's out of pocket cost vary based on provider selected; Tier 1 provider: $25.00 copayment, Tier 2 provider: $75.00 copayment.

Multiple factors contributed to the narrow networks' lackluster cost-containing performance, including:

- System fragmentation,
- Reimbursement methodologies,
- Limited technology, and
- Generous benefit plan design.

System fragmentation refers to the way the healthcare system is organized—by site of service and by specialty fueled cost then and now. Regardless of the type of network, the reimbursement models used, providers were primarily paid with a discounted fee-for-service. Fee-for-service is a volume-based model: the more one does the more one makes without accountability for quality or outcomes. A further mitigating factor was the information technology used by providers lacked the necessary sophistication to decipher cost-efficiency and quality metrics for a given population. Product and benefit design involving low copayments and low out-of-pocket deductibles provided little financial disincentive to seek and receive care. It was not uncommon for the "worried well patient" to seek care for a $5.00 or $10.00 office copayment.

As premiums continued their upward spiral, payers crafted new product offerings, such as high-deductible or consumer-driven plans. High-deductible plans place greater financial burden on patients, which theoretically incentivizes them to become engaged consumers. Consumer-driven plans were embraced by employers as a means to share in or offload these increased premiums. The chart below depicts the increase in high deductible health plans.[2]

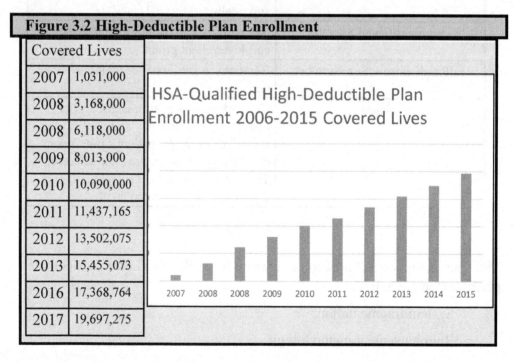

Figure 3.2 High-Deductible Plan Enrollment

Covered Lives	
2007	1,031,000
2008	3,168,000
2008	6,118,000
2009	8,013,000
2010	10,090,000
2011	11,437,165
2012	13,502,075
2013	15,455,073
2016	17,368,764
2017	19,697,275

HSA-Qualified High-Deductible Plan Enrollment 2006-2015 Covered Lives

Much has changed in the new value-based payment environment. Information technology has advanced, allowing payers to measure quality metrics and determine cost of care. From the 1990s to today it is not uncommon for providers to intuitively state:

2 "2015 Census of Health Savings Account - High Deductible Health Plans." AHIP Center for Policy and Research. Accessed Oct 7, 2016. https://ahip.org/wp-content/uploads/2015/11/HSA_Report.pdf

- "My" patients are sicker
- "My" patients aren't hospitalized
- "My" patients receive the highest quality care
- "My" patients don't go to the Emergency Room
- "My" patients like me

So who are the patients included in the "my"? Providers referred to all patients they recalled in their practice to whom they provided care regardless of insurance carrier. Payers defined "my" for their HMO products when the patient selected a primary care provider or primary care practice. These two populations could not be more different! Additionally, most payers today have the ability to track and quantify provider performance relative to cost and quality and compare peer groups.

A common characteristic of both the providers' and payers' definition of "my" was this—both referred to patients seen and for whom care was provided. Advances in information technology allow payers to identify an 'attribute' patients enrolled in, products such as PPOs that do not require them to select a primary care provider at enrollment to a specific provider. This shift in healthcare is significant, the denominator has changed. It is no longer limited to the patient seen; it extends and includes patients not seen, defined as a population.

Today's information technology allows payers to use and aggregate claim data to **severity adjust** a provider's population, resulting in a "known case mix" or "burden of illness." The provider is compared to a peer group, generally of the same specialty. Through the use of data, payers can share the provider's specific case mix or severity adjustment scores. Prudent providers will embrace this opportunity to substantiate or dispel their intuition regarding the severity of illness for their patient population.

The proliferation of narrow networks has been further fueled by the ACA. The provisions of the ACA span over multiple years, 2010-2020. In terms of provisions, 2011 and 2014 were impactful years. Twenty provisions were slotted to become effective in 2011 with 16 targeted to become effective in 2014. In terms of substantial impact, the 2014 provisions created sweeping change, ultimately leveling the insurance playing field. As we delve into several of the provisions that became effective in 2014, it becomes crystal clear why narrow networks are growing in popularity.

Figure 3.3[3] ACA Provisions and Requirements

ACA Provision— Effective January 1, 2014	Requirement(s)
Individual requirement to have health insurance	Requires U.S. citizens and legal residents to have qualifying health coverage (there is a phased-in tax penalty for those without coverage, with certain exemptions).
Health Insurance Exchanges	Creates state-based American Health Benefit Exchanges and Small Business Health Options Program (SHOP) Exchanges, administered by a governmental agency or non-profit organization, through which individuals and small businesses with up to 100 employees can purchase qualified coverage. Exchanges will have a single form for applying for health programs, including coverage through the Exchanges and Medicaid and CHIP programs.
Health Insurance Premiums and Cost Subsidies	Provides refundable and advanceable tax credits and cost sharing subsidies to eligible individuals. Premium subsidies are available to families with incomes between 133-400 percent of the federal poverty level to purchase insurance through the Exchanges, while cost sharing subsidies are available to those with incomes up to 250 percent of the poverty level.
Guaranteed Availability of Coverage	Requires guarantee issue and renewability of health insurance regardless of health status and allows rating variation based only on age (limited to a 3 to 1 ratio), geographic area, family composition, and tobacco use (limited to 1.5. to 1 ratio) in the individual and the small group market and the Exchanges.
No Annual Limits on Coverage	Prohibits annual limits on the dollar value of coverage.
Essential Health Benefits	Creates an essential health benefits package that provides a comprehensive set of services, limiting annual cost-sharing to the Health Savings Account limits ($5,950/individual and $11,900/family in 2010). Creates four categories of plans to be offered through the Exchanges, and in the individual and small group markets, varying based on the proportion of plan benefits they cover.

---

3 "Hospital Networks: Configurations on the Exchanges and Their Impact on Premiums." Accessed October 7, 2016. http://healthcare.mckinsey.com/sites/default/files/Hospital_Networks_Configurations_on_the_Exchanges_and_Their_Impact_on_Premiums.pdf

So, what is a payer to do? The ACA presented the payers with the potential for opportunity to grow membership, however with this opportunity came inherent financial risk. The major payers evaluated the business need to participate in the new market place: public health insurance exchanges. Aetna, Cigna and UnitedHealthcare treaded cautiously, participating and offering products in limited states, whereas WellPoint took a broader approach, participating more fully in multiple states. The new marketplace was filled with many unknowns such as who would enroll and how sick were they. Large carriers don't have a high tolerance for unknown risk or financial losses. For the carriers that elected to participate, the majority offered products through a narrow network, with many offering products through an ultra-narrow network.[4]

> The competitive logic behind narrow networks goes like this: ACA marketplaces require that qualified health plans with comparable actuarial value (at platinum, gold, silver, and bronze levels) display their costs side by side in online insurance marketplaces. This makes it easier than ever before to compare health plans, and creates unparalleled pressures on insurance companies to keep their prices down so as to attract new customers.[5]

In the past, carriers designed limited benefit plans and utilized stringent underwriting guidelines limiting unhealthy individuals from accessing coverage, essentially cherry-picking the healthy individuals. The ACA levels the playing field by requiring payers to offer similar, comparable benefits and to insure all individuals with preexisting conditions and/or increased health risk. The end result is payers will compete on price, and therefore they will need to control and contain costs.

Multiple avenues exist to create a narrow network. Costlier hospitals and higher-cost providers may be excluded. "In 2015 almost 50 percent of all plans offered on health insurance exchanges have narrow networks, and almost 20 percent are considered 'ultra-narrow networks,' which give consumers even fewer doctor and hospital choices."[6]

---

4 Blumenthal, M.D. David. "Reflecting on Health Reform-Narrow Networks: Boon or Bane?" - The Commonwealth Fund. Accessed September 21, 2016. http://www.commonwealthfund.org/publications/blog/2014/feb/narrows-networks-boon-or-bane

5 Akshay Kapur, Ashish Kaura, Minoo Javanmardian, Paolo Borromeo. "Private Health Insurance Exchanges: Fueling the "consumerization" of Employer sponsored Health Insurance." Accessed September 21, 2016. http://www.strategyand.pwc.com/reports/emergence-private-health-insurance-exchanges

6 Overland Dina. "More consumers enrolling in narrow network health insurance plans." Accessed October 9, 2016. http://www.fiercehealthcare.com/payer/more-consumers-enrolling-narrow-network-health-insurance-plans

Benefit models are driving this transformation in an accelerated fashion. For decades, U.S. companies that offer healthcare benefits to employees have stuck to a defined benefits model in which the company offers a standard set of health benefits and shoulders most of the financial burden and risk of healthcare cost. Over the past decade, this model has come under increasing strain as healthcare costs have more than doubled, creating an affordability crisis for employers. The problem has reached a tipping point. Some employers are considering a paradigm shift to their health benefits strategy akin to the transition from pension plans to 401(k) accounts: switching from defined benefits toward a defined contribution model. Instead of designing and offering delineated health benefits, companies will make cash contributions to savings accounts that employees use to purchase the insurance products of their choice. This model allows the company to cap its healthcare cost at a desired threshold, improving control of current expenses and future liabilities.

In addition to the affordability problem, the employer-sponsored insurance landscape is also being altered by healthcare reform, particularly the establishment of the individual mandate and public health insurance exchanges. Healthcare reform specifically aims to make health insurance more affordable for individuals and small businesses; however, midsized and large employers might decide to use these public exchanges to control their own costs, terminating their insurance and routing employees to the public exchanges. This would compress payer margins and force payers to respond defensively with alternative solutions such as defined contribution plans and private exchanges. Meanwhile, intermediaries, such as benefits consultants, can also strengthen their role in the value chain by offering solutions that help employers of all sizes control costs.[7]

Initially, when the payers introduced products and provider networks, many using narrow and or ultra-narrow networks, physicians shared their perspective—they did not care to participate in the plans being offered on the exchange and did not anticipate the financial impact it would have on their practice. Many providers thought the products being offered would be limited to the public exchange. Separate from the ACA, so-called "private exchanges" have emerged as an option for employers providing coverage to their workers. These private exchanges do not provide access to premium subsidies like the public exchanges, nor do they necessarily involve standardized coverage tiers.

---

7 Alvarado, Alex, and Matthew Rai. "Examining Private Exchanges in the Employer-Sponsored Insurance Market." Accessed October 7, 2016. http://files.kff.org/attachment/examining-private-exchanges-in-the-employer-sponsored-insurance-market-report

Private exchanges are marketplaces of health insurance and other related products. Employers purchase health insurance through the private exchange, and then their employees can choose a health plan from those supplied by participating payers. The value proposition of private exchanges differs from public

exchanges in some important ways. First, private exchanges are flexible and can be customized to address the needs of any employer group, unlike public exchanges, which are targeted to individuals and small groups. For instance, private exchanges can design benefits tiers specific to employer segments with robust multichannel employee decision support. Another advantage is that private exchanges can offer a broader range of retail products—such as dental and life insurance, and even non-insurance products—that public exchanges cannot. At this time, two private exchange models are emerging:

Single-carrier exchanges: These exchanges are promoted by a single payer and target employers that wish to maintain some role in choosing both the insurance carrier and plan design. Depending on how involved employers want to be in benefits design and negotiation, products may be customized and priced for the employee group or individuals.

Multi-carrier exchanges: These exchanges, predominantly promoted by third-party intermediaries such as brokers or benefits consultants, will provide a broad range of payer and plan design options and encourage employers to take a more hands-off role. For payers, multi-carrier exchanges that list individual products on a menu of offerings pose commoditization risk that could squeeze payer margins.[8]

The healthcare affordability crisis continues to be a primary concern for most employers as well as individuals purchasing healthcare. Payers offering products on the public exchange or through a private exchange will compete on cost, the majority of payers will elect to deliver their products through a narrow network with the goal to contain cost and deliver quality.

---

[8] "2014 PCMH Program Performance Report." July 30, 2015. Accessed September 21, 2016. https://member.carefirst.com/carefirst-resources/pdf/pcmh-program-performance-report-2014.pdf

Figure 3.4 Emerging Exchange Types

Defined contribution insurance

		Single-carrier exchange	Multi-carrier exchange
Overview	Description	Exchanges promoted by payors to give members and employers access to their products (group products)	Exchanges designed to link consumers and employers to a variety of benefits plans across several payors (individual products)
	Emerging players	Bloom/WellPoint/HCSC/BCBS Michigan BlueCross BlueShield of Minnesota Highmark Towers Watson	ADP AON Hewitt CaliforniaChoice eHealthinsurance Extend Health Health Connector Walgreens
Employee value proposition	Group or individual products	Group (likely) Individual (possible)	Individual (likely) Group (possible)
	Level of decision support	High	Varied
	Number of plan options	~3–5 (one carrier)	~10+ (across carriers)
Employer value proposition	Employer involvement	Passive to active	Passive
	Administrative burden	Medium to high	Medium
	Relationship with carrier	High	Low to medium

Another emerging model is that of the primary care providers defining a narrow network. In this scenario, the payer establishes incentives around cost/quality and it is up to the primary care provider to refer patients to their top picks. Incentives are typically shared savings associated with value-based contracts and referral patterns in terms of network—which is a key component of performance. Beginning in 2011, CareFirst, BCBS in the Mid-Atlantic region developed a PCMH Performance Program whereby:

- No narrow networks were used,

- Primary care physicians (PCPs) referred where they believe they would get the best result, and

- Providers were rewarded with increases in fee-for-service reimbursement dependent upon quality scores and savings.

As of 2014, this strategy bent the cost curve by 2 percent - 3 percent, results which exceeded payer expectations.[9] Regardless of the presence of a payer constructed narrow network or one driven by primary care providers, practices should appreciate that these powerful steering mechanisms can have a profound effect on sustainability and future growth. Understanding the how & why of narrow networks will assist in preparing a value-based contracting strategy.

---

9 "2014 PCMH Program Performance Report." July 30, 2015. Accessed September 21, 2016. https://member.carefirst.com/carefirst-resources/pdf/pcmh-program-performance-report-2014.pdf

Chapter 4

Patient Liability

Increasing patient liability accelerated by the ACA has emerged as a major trend in healthcare. This is part of the market forces driving the industry from volume-based to value-based care, coupled with increasing high-deductible health plans moving us toward achieving the Triple Aim. Consumers exercise greater caution in spending when the dollars come more directly from their pocket, according to The Rand Corporation.[1] This trend of placing more financial responsibility on patients for medical services has a profound impact on medical practices.

From a contracting perspective, the allowables negotiated in agreements represent a much smaller portion than ever before. According to MGMA, $1 out of every $4 comes directly from the patient.[2] Practices must consider these implications for their financial health and a practice's contracts can add a layer of complexity. Practices that successfully manage within this framework are keenly aware of the differences among insurance policies/products and rigorously engage in service collection.

So, how can managed-care contracts impact collection of patient liability? First, when evaluating collection percentages (e.g., gross collections, which is the total amount paid compared to total charges) by payer, the amounts received in terms of revenue are comprised of both patient and payer payments. The allowed amount is what is possible in terms of potential revenue and the ever-increasing shift of portions relative to payer payment and patient payment impact this metric. Take a look at this scenario:

---

1 Focus, By Policy. "Paying for Healthcare." Paying for Care: In Depth. Accessed September 21, 2016. http://www.rand.org/health/key-topics/paying-for-care/in-depth.html

2 Pope, Christina, and Jim Margolis. "Perpective on Patient Payments." MGMA Connexion. April 2010. http://www.mgma.com/Libraries/Assets/PracticeResources/Publications/MG-MAConnexion/2010/Perspective-on-patient-payments-MGMA-Connexion-April-2010.pdf

Figure 4.1 Patient Collection Impact on Contract Performance

CPT	Charge	Allowable	Payer Paid	Patient Paid	Patient Portion
99213	$200	$ 70	$ 50	$ ----	$ 20
Gross Collections		Total Charges	Total Payment if Patient Portion not Collected	Ratio	
		$200	$ 50	25%	
Gross Collections		Total Charges	Total Payment if Patient Portion Collected	Ratio	
		$200	$ 70	35%	

Essentially, the contracts could have identical allowed amounts, but if patient liability is greater in one than the other and collection efforts are not up to par, then contract performance interpretation could be skewed by the ability to collect patient liability. This is an important consideration when optimizing a contracting strategy. Use "allowed amounts" and not "payments collected" to evaluate contract performance.

Additionally, there are many other factors to consider relative to patient collections, such as: retro-eligibility considerations, eligibility verification, grace periods, non-covered services and contract language that limits deposit collections. This varies payer to payer. In some instances, provisions will be spelled out in the contract. The details may also be incorporated into the provider manuals. In order to position the practice to manage this piece of the reimbursement puzzle, examine and understand these areas as part of the contract evaluation process.

In terms of eligibility, the onus is on the practice to verify eligibility and simply checking that eligibility has been verified is not enough to support a rigorous time-of-service collections program. If a patient has a high deductible, verifying coverage is the first step, but determining the amount to be collected requires investigation into the deductible and how much of the deductible the patient has met. Understanding the complete picture in terms of what should be collected at the time of service will have a positive impact on a practice's cash flow.

Some managed-care agreements contain clauses that authorize the payer to refuse payment or to retroactively take back payments for services if eligibility is not verified. Also, payers may confirm eligibility, then later determine that the validation was in error and recoup the payment after services were provided. Additionally, the payer may conclude that the patient obtained services deceitfully, having knowledge that they were not eligible at the time of service. Relative to non-covered services, practices must identify these in advance of providing services; it is a best practice and often a contractual obligation to obtain consent from the patient prior to rendering services. Nailing down financial obligations up front is critical to ensuring that the practice is paid for services provided. The responsibility lies with the practice to bill the patients for services (covered and non-covered) and collect the appropriate amounts due in the most proactive manner possible.

An issue that further contributes to this burden is the 90-day grace periods for the exchange products. Typically, commercial products provide a 30-day grace period for a member to pay a premium before coverage is terminated. For healthcare exchange products, if a patient pays at least the first month's premium of the year, in any subsequent month the patient has three months to make the premium payment before coverage is terminated.[3] So a patient could pay premiums for one month and not in subsequent months and may appear to have coverage.

If a practice provides care during a period where the patient did not pay premiums, they may be challenged to pursue the patient for reimbursement for services provided. Insurers are required to pay claims for the first month of the grace period and notify healthcare providers that they may not be paid for the second and third months of the grace period. If the patient does not pay all premiums for the three-month period, coverage is terminated only to the end of the first month of the grace period.[4]

Ultimately, from a practice perspective, tracking down a patient once services have been provided and collecting months in arrears does not typically yield positive results. Once a patient leaves a practice, the possibility of collecting decreases dramatically and practices are collecting more at time of service that ever before as depicted in the chart on the next page: (Figure 4.2)

Instituting rigorous time-of-service collections protocols is imperative for practices given the ever-increasing revenue stream apportioned to patients. From a contracting perspective, the practice should attempt to negotiate a provision that guarantees payment for services rendered in good faith to patients who are later determined to not be eligible if the practice follows eligibility verification proto-

3 "How Consumers Might Game The 90-Day Grace Period And What Can Be Done About It." Health Affairs. Accessed September 21, 2016. http://healthaffairs.org/blog/2014/11/17/how-consumers-might-game-the-90-day-grace-period-and-what-can-be-done-about-it/

4 Ibid

cols and the payer delivers inadequate or untimely information. Also, the agreement should not limit the ability to collect from patients at the time of service. State statues may also address timelines for recoupment. Above all, the practice should work to optimize the time of service collections workflows internally in order to capture the dollars due and maximize overall contract performance.

Figure 4.2[5] Average Percentage Revenue Collected at Time-of-Service

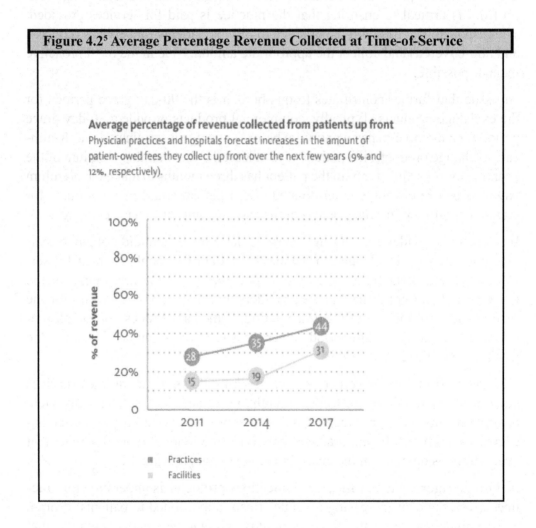

Average percentage of revenue collected from patients up front
Physician practices and hospitals forecast increases in the amount of patient-owed fees they collect up front over the next few years (9% and 12%, respectively).

5 "Consumerism Driving Big Changes to Patient Collection Practices for Providers." Accessed September 21, 2016. https://www.availity.com/about-us/news-center/consumerism-driving-big-changes-to-patient-collections-practices-for-providers

Chapter 5

Transparency

Transparency is making information about quality and cost available to patients before services are provided. When people have access to information, they become smart consumers. Technology puts information at the consumer's fingertips, vastly enhancing transparency. For example, many use Yelp to review ratings for all types for services, which now also includes healthcare providers. This ease of accessibility and cultural shift to obtaining reviews before making purchasing decisions fuels transparency.

U.S. healthcare costs rise 8 percent to 10 percent annually; we spend billions of dollars a year on healthcare. It is estimated that 30 percent of this spending is wasted.[1] If that's true, how do we align incentives to decrease the waste? One of the primary goals of value-based contracting is aimed at decreasing this 30 percent waste, in addition to increasing quality and improving outcomes. These next-generation managed care contracts are focused on rewarding providers for decreasing waste. For example, payers provide aggregated quality and cost data, demonstrating options to offer the same quality of care at a lower cost. Waste can include:

- Services provided in a costlier care setting
- Duplicative services
- Inappropriate service
- Unnecessary services

For example, referring a patient to a hospital setting for a CT scan instead of a free-standing imaging center would be considered wasteful. Was the service previously performed and/or is it the most appropriate

---

1 "Using Technology to Cure Enterprise Healthcare." Accessed September 21, 2016. http://content.castlighthealth.com/rs/castlighthealth/images/EHCeBook.pdf

and necessary service? Quality is maintained and delivered in the most cost-efficient, appropriate setting. Transparency has the potential to lower costs and is very much part of value-based contracting initiatives.

CMS continues to build upon the tools provided through the ACA to advance transparency in our health care system. Hospital Compare and Physician Compare information is available today and provides limited information. In the future, the Physician Compare website (https://www.medicare.gov/physiciancompare/) will reflect scores for each clinician related to quality and cost. The scores will be available to all healthcare consumers including patients, payers, hospitals and other practices.[2] Under MACRA, reimbursement for medical care is in part tied to performance quality and cost efficiency programs.

When creating a contracting strategy, it's critically important for providers/practices to understand how their performance compares to their peer group. If favorable, these results may become a useful tool in contract negotiation. In terms of gathering this intelligence, providers can access Quality and Resource Use Reports (QRURs) from CMS, which provide detailed information around quality and cost of care. Once MACRA begins, similar reports will be available and accessible and will contact additional episodic payment information. These data sets are powerful resources for practices to use in order to better compare a practice to peer groups.

In concert with payers' focus, patients are beginning to appreciate the premise that the greater the financial responsibility, the more discerning the buyer. This tends to be true in many aspects of life. For example, a teenager thinks more carefully about purchasing a pair of jeans when they are the ones who must pay. This may influence them to save up for an expensive pair, or compel them to make do with a cheaper pair so they can save their money for something else. Theoretically, it is the alignment of incentives that drives the behavior. This now plays out on a daily basis with purchasers of healthcare services across the nation. The central idea is that providing cost, quality and other information to consumers before services are rendered may have a positive impact on the overall cost curve, while preserving quality/outcomes.

Many transparency tools are available through apps and payer websites (i.e., Aetna, Cigna, UnitedHealthcare and many BCBS plans) as cost estimator tools that report prices for the individual elements of an episode of care, such as facility costs, surgeon's prices, costs of durable medical equipment (DME) and more.

2 Blum, Jonathan. "Next Steps in Medicare Data Trasnparency." Accessed September 21, 2016. http://blog.cms.gov/2014/04/02/next-steps-in-medicare-data-transparency/

This information, along with accolades and payer ratings, is made available to patients. It's important to note that research suggest that consumer choice is impacted by information pertaining to cost and quality in an interesting way. Judith Hibbard, D.P.H., senior researcher at the Health Policy Research Group, University of Oregon, was the lead author of a study that sought to determine how different presentations of cost and quality information affected the likelihood that consumers would make high-value choices.

> The study, which involved 1,421 consumers, found that significant numbers of respondents—though not a majority—viewed higher cost as a proxy for higher quality. This was true even among those with high-deductible health plans that would expose them to a higher share of costs. But when the cost and quality information was reported side by side in an easy-to-interpret format, more respondents made high-value choices. Labels indicating that providers made "appropriate usage" of resources or were "careful with your healthcare dollars" also led more people to choose high-value providers. [3]

The take away here is to be sure that if a practice has accolades, quality scores, accreditations that attest to being a high-quality provider—make sure that information is reflected appropriately.

There are also many private-label transparency tools available to consumers (i.e. Compass Smart Shopper, Castlight, Change Healthcare and Healthcare Bluebook) that incorporate the following qualitative features including but not limited to: highlight Centers of Excellence, provide economic incentives to patients who use high-quality/low-cost resources, and make available reference-based pricing demonstrating price variances. So expect that a practice's cost, ratings, along with any accolades (i.e., Patient Centered Medical Home accreditation), may be present within these tools. Patients likely will use this information to facilitate purchasing decisions. Although new, some of these tools are very innovative. For example, Change Healthcare proactively alerts people via text or e-mail if they have an opportunity to save money on routine care or prescription drugs.

> We look at consumers' existing claims data and identify opportunities for savings," says Doug Ghertner, the company's president. "A message might say, 'You can save $250 a year on your health care costs,' for example, and then provide instructions about how to look up lower-cost providers. Some of the alerts incorporate principles of behavioral economics such as loss aversion or

---

3 J. H. Hibbard, J. Greene, S. Sofaer et al., "An Experiment Shows That a Well-Designed Report on Costs and Quality Can Help Consumers Choose High-Value Health Care," Health Affairs, March 2012 31(3):560–68

social norming to incite action: "Did you know that your peers are spending $500 less than you are on their blood sugar tests?"[4]

Additionally, Healthcare Bluebook, which is freely available to consumers, publishes what it determines to be a fair price for various medical services, based on a review of claims data and other consumer-submitted reports. Employers and health plans can pay for access to a version that lists in-network providers ranked by value. "Recently, Healthcare Blue Book launched a subscription service for patient-centered medical homes, so that primary care physicians can work with their patients to make referrals to high-quality, lower-cost providers."[5] Being aware of a practice's cost for care and how referral patterns impact that cost is an important consideration. Positioning for value-based contracting must include an understanding of a practice's cost and the cost of care given your patient population. This will have bearing on construction of the practice's Value Proposition.

---

4 Hostetter, Martha and Sarah Klein. "Health Care Price Transparency: Can It Promote High-Value Care?" - The Commonwealth Fund. Accessed September 21, 2016. http://www.commonwealthfund.org/publications/newsletters/quality-matters/2012/april-may/in-focus.
5 Ibid

Chapter 6

Quality Metrics

Quality measurement in healthcare is the process of using data to evaluate the performance of health plans and healthcare providers against recognized quality standards.[1] These measures can take many forms and evaluate care across a wide range of healthcare settings, from medical practices to hospital systems. Quality measures are central to ranking health plans and providers and are used by CMS in payment calculations for Medicare beneficiaries through the Physician Quality Reporting System (PQRS) and the value-based payment modifier and soon in the Quality Payment Program.

In terms of striving for the Triple Aim, measuring healthcare quality is a foundational step in the process of improving healthcare quality. Currently, the quality of care received in the United States is substandard: Patients receive the proper diagnosis and care only about 55 percent of the time,[2] and wide variations in healthcare quality, access, and outcomes persist.[3] Quality metrics are a baseline measure that can assist in improving care through identifying gaps in care as well as other areas in need of improvement (e.g., patient satisfaction).

At a high level, quality measures generally fall into one of the following categories:

- Structure
- Process

---

1 "Measuring Health Care Quality." Accessed September 21, 2016. http://familiesusa.org/sites/default/files/product_documents/HSI Quality Measurement_Brief_final_web.pdf
2 Elizabeth McGlynn, Stephen Asch, John Adams, et al., "The Quality of Care Delivered to Adults in the United States," The New England Journal of Medicine 348, no. 26 (June 2003): 2,641, available online at http://www.nejm.org/doi/full/10.1056/NEJMsa022615.
3 Agency for Healthcare Research and Quality, 2012 National Health Care Quality Report (Rockville, MD: Department of Health and Human Services, May 2013), available online at http://www.ahrq.gov/research/findings/nhqrdr/nhqr12/2012nhqr.pdf

- Outcome

- Patient Experience

Structural measures focus on characteristics of a care setting, including facilities, personnel, and/or policies and procedures related to care delivery. Process measures focus on identifying whether services provided to patients are consistent with common clinical care standards. Outcomes measures evaluate patient health as a result of care received, and patient experience gauges overall patient satisfaction with their healthcare experience.[4] In most instances, health plans use measures in each of the categories to rank healthcare providers within each of their respective quality programs.

Payers utilize metrics from many origins including: HEDIS, National Quality Forum (NQF), Agency for Healthcare Research and Quality (AHRQ), Consumer Assessment of Healthcare Providers and Systems (CAHPS), Patient-Centered Outcomes Research Institute (PCORI) and others. Sometimes, professional societies, such as the American Heart Association (AHA) or the American College of Surgeons (ACS), identify a mass of evidence relative to a treatment and become involved in developing clinical guidelines that end up becoming standards of care for diseases and conditions. After a measure is developed, it is often endorsed by organizations like the NQF and others.

Many payers use HEDIS data as a primary measurement source. This data becomes a focal point of most health plan "report cards" that appear in national magazines and local newspapers. Health plans also use HEDIS results themselves to see where they need to focus their improvement efforts.

HEDIS measures address a broad range of important health issues. Among them are the following:

- Asthma medication use

- Persistence of beta-blocker treatment after a heart attack

- Controlling high blood pressure

- Comprehensive diabetes care

- Breast cancer screening

- Antidepressant medication management

- Childhood and adolescent immunization status

- Childhood and adult weight/BMI assessment

---

4 "Measuring Health Care Quality." Accessed September 21, 2016. http://familiesusa.org/sites/default/files/product_documents/HSI Quality Measurement_Brief_final_web.pdf.

The HEDIS tool is used by more than 90 percent of America's health plans to measure performance on important dimensions of care and service. Altogether, HEDIS consists of 81 measures across five domains of care.[5]

A practice can identify the common threads among payer programs starting with HEDIS measures in order to identify commonality and overlap of metrics. It is critical for providers to understand their performance related to payer quality metrics initiatives.

What do quality measures have to do with managed care contract negotiations? As previously presented in Chapter 3 Narrow Networks, today's technology allows payers to use data to profile providers. Frequently performance related to quality metrics are integral components of most payers quality management programs. Much of this data is being made publicly available through transparency initiatives like CMS's Physician Compare, as already discussed. Patients are using this information to make decisions around where to receive care, and providers on where to refer patients. While practices may not currently get this information in granular form from payers, it is becoming increasingly available. Many payers produce this information and provide it via a portal and/or will sit down and walk through the information with the practice.

In some states, statutes dictate that quality data must be provided to the provider before the information is made publicly available and the provider has the right to review the data and request backup details and request reconsideration. As part of the managed care contracting process, practices must understand how they perform compared to peer groups in terms of quality metrics. Many of the new value-based contracting methodologies contain a threshold for quality that unlocks financial incentives. Without considering quality metrics, even if there is cost savings, there may not be shared savings or increases provided without achieving the quality thresholds. Later chapters will go into further detail about how to gather and incorporate this type of information into a practice's managed care contracting strategy.

---

5 "HEDIS & Quality Measurement." What Is HEDIS. Accessed September 21, 2016. http://www.ncqa.org/hedis-quality-measurement/what-is-hedis

Chapter 7

Connecting the Dots

In the introduction, we discussed payer common themes. In order for medical practices to effectively position for the future, it's necessary to understand the driving forces that are catapulting our healthcare system into new territory. Escalating healthcare costs and the surge in baby boomers becoming Medicare eligible both contribute to creating the affordability crisis. Despite the high costs, Americans are not healthier when compared to other countries. This negatively impacts our economy as U.S. businesses and the Federal Government spend far more on healthcare than other countries, compromising our ability to compete in the global market.[1]

The ACA was created to transition the current healthcare system by increasing the affordability and rate of health insurance coverage for Americans while reducing overall costs of health care and improving quality of care. The implementation of MACRA and new reimbursement models piloted through Medicare and Medicaid are accelerators for commercial payers as their customers are demanding high value/lower costs. While providers are actively participating with CMS and local state programs, now is the time to leverage practice value with commercial payers and carve a new path that rewards a practice for being part of this transformation. It starts with understanding where the practice wants to be on the Managed Care Contracting Continuum and charting a course to get there.

---

1 CEOs: Health Costs Disadvantage U.S. In Global Economy." Health Affairs. Accessed September 21, 2016. http://healthaffairs.org/blog/2009/03/13/ceos-health-costs-disadvantage-us-in-global-economy/

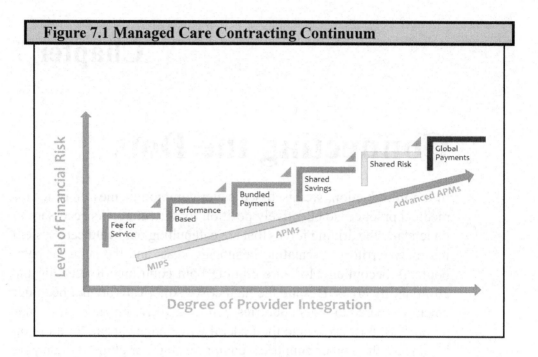

Figure 7.1 Managed Care Contracting Continuum

Let's quickly connect the dots:

- **The Triple Aim** – core of most value-based initiatives focusing on decreasing costs, improving health and the patient experience

- **Narrow Networks** – used by providers, payers and/or employers to steer patients to panels of providers identified as being high value and low cost

- **Increasing Patient Liability** – cost shifting from payers to patients driving accelerated engagement and discernment about where, who and how they receive healthcare

- **Transparency** – mechanisms for communicating value and cost of providers to consumers and purchasers of healthcare

- **Quality Metrics** – measurements of how a provider performs compared to peer groups in terms of meeting quality standards

Value-based contracting is about aligning incentives with the goal of creating a relationship with a payer/network/employer that will reward the practice for effectively implementing the Triple Aim. The healthcare industry is in the midst of reinventing itself from its very core in an attempt to move toward the Triple

Aim. This transformation involves a number of considerations for providers to contemplate including: identification of high-quality/low cost-providers through quality metrics/cost comparisons, claims based outcome data implications, consumer education regarding provider performance, and increasing patient liability, driving transformation ultimately through the patient. Now that we have discussed how these core components connect, we will begin to examine the different value-based payment models to be considered.

Chapter 8

Fee-for-Service

Managed Care Contracting Continuum: Fee-for-Service

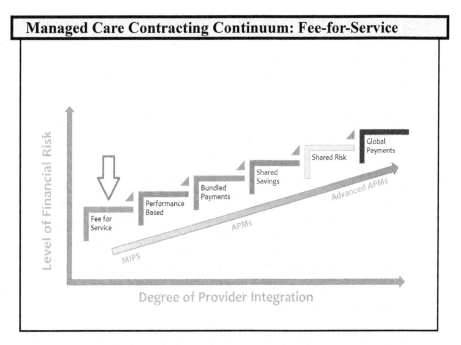

Fee-for-service or discounted fee-for-service refers to the payment for each service rendered by a provider based on a discounted, negotiated fee. This discount is granted in exchange for referral. While the transition to value-based reimbursement models is well underway, fee-for-service remains one of the most common reimbursement models today. Fee-for-service reimbursement appears in many value-based reimbursement methodologies, with the drivers and incentives structured around value and not volume.

Various types of fee schedule foundations are used in discounted fee-for-service reimbursement methodologies:

- Medicare Physician Fee Schedules

- Workers' Compensation fee schedules

- Usual and customary rates

- Payer proprietary fee schedules

- Discount off billed charges

- Case rates

- Blend of any/all of the above

Many of these schedules are based on well-understood algorithms while others are not. For example, Medicare fee schedules are commonly used in fee schedule development and are standard for a given geography. The Medicare Physician Fee Schedule (PFS) (also known as Part B fee schedule) is based on the resource-based relative value system (RBRVS) and is adjusted through geographic practice cost indexes (GPCIs).[1] The RBRVS uses relative value units (RVUs) which are intended to reflect the relative level of time, practice expense, skill, training and intensity required by a provider to deliver a service. RVUs are comprised of:

- **Work RVU**, reflecting the relative time and intensity associated with furnishing a Medicare PFS service. It accounts for approximately 50 percent of the total payment associated with a service;

- **Practice Expense RVU** (PE), which reflects the costs of maintaining a practice (such as renting office space, buying supplies and equipment, and staff costs); and

- **Malpractice RVU** (MP), reflecting the costs of malpractice insurance.[2]

These factors are then multiplied by the established conversion factor (CF) for a given time period to determine allowed amounts.

Figure 8.1 Medicare PFS Payment Rates Formula

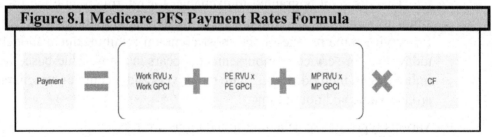

1 Medicare Physician Fee Schedule: Payment System Fact Sheet Series. Accessed September 21, 2016. https://www.cms.gov/Outreach-and-Education/Medicare-Learning-Network-MLN/MLNProducts/downloads/MedcrephysFeeSchedfctsht.pdf

2 Ibid

Commercial payers often employ a given span of Medicare years (one or more) to establish the basis of a fee schedule.

Other foundations are less transparent. Usual, Customary and Reasonable (UCR) rates can be based on purchased data (such as OptumInsight aka Ingenix), average wholesale price and/or payer-determined amounts along with many other possibilities. Payers also create their own fee schedules based on claim data, UCR and/or other proprietary methods. Case rates can be created (these are also known as bundles, discussed in Chapter 10) and reflected with a fee-for-service arrangement for a group of services. Payers may also reimburse based on a provider's billed charges, which are nonstandard and can vary widely. This is typically performed as a discount off a charge and may apply to an entire fee schedule or for a selection of CPT codes within a fee schedule, or may be used to reimburse for CPT codes that do not have an established rate (e.g., new CPT codes).

Commercial payers frequently group CPT codes in bands or in a service category, and can blend many different methodologies to construct a provider reimbursement schema.

Commercial payers frequently combine multiple fee for service methodologies to create an entire fee schedule. By way of an example, a payer may reimburse a specific band of CPT codes such as Evaluation and Management codes at 103 percent of current year RBRVS and reimburse CPT codes for radiology procedures at 100 percent based on a different year of Medicare and so on. Services for physical therapy may be reimbursed on a case or per-visit rate. Prudent providers demonstrate a strong understanding of the various reimbursement possibilities by service category within the fee schedule. Additionally, they have clear understanding of how their high frequency CPT codes will be reimbursed.

These can be simple or complex depending on the payer and the practice. Hierarchies—where one fee schedule may apply if a condition is met and a different schedule might be used if it is not met—might also be used. For example, in the following chart (next page), CPT codes included in the category Other Drugs may be paid at 95 percent of Medicare. If no rate is established, it would be paid at 100 percent of WAC or 98 percent of AWP and so on. Furthermore, segments of the reimbursement category may fluctuate. Vaccine rates, for example, if based on Centers for Disease Control and Prevention (CDC) sector pricing could change when that fee schedule is updated. It can be very difficult to determine what a provider will be paid without a detailed code-by-code analysis.

Figure 8.2 Sample Partial Rate Attachment	
Service Category	**Pricing Source & Rate**
Specialty Pharmacy Drugs	100% Specialty Pharmacy Reimbursement Rate
Other CDC Vaccines	110% of CDC Private Sector Pricing
Other Drugs	95% Medicare Part B Fee Schedule, or 100% Wholesale Acquisition Cost (WAC), or 98% Average Wholesale Price (AWP), or 75% of your charge, or 100% usual and customary

Key Attributes

Historically, commercial payers, Medicare and Medicaid have utilized fee-for-service as the primary reimbursement model to pay providers. Today, this is commonly referred to as pay for volume. The key attributes of this reimbursement method are as follows:

- Administratively simple
- Financially safe
- Payer edit logic applies
- Professional and facility services are billed separately
- Payment is retrospective
- Low data analytics required
- No clinical or administrative integration required
- No penalties for cost inefficiencies or quality outcomes

Managed Care Organizations (MCOs) have been using a discounted fee-for-service reimbursement methodology for years. This form of reimbursement is fairly easy to administer for both the provider and the MCO: both parties reach agreement based on a negotiated fee schedule, and the provider bills for services and receives reimbursement from the MCO. Practices need to monitor negotiated rates to ensure reimbursement is accurate. At first glance, monitoring for payment accuracy may appear straight forward and simple. Accounting for various nuances that may occur within the fee schedule often present challenges, for example, fixed reimbursement for specific CPT 4 codes, case rates and multiple surgical guidelines. Frequently providers default to accepting the allowed amount paid. In contrast strong practices load and maintain contract allowables by payer into their practice management software. Overall contract performance should be monitored and contracts should be negotiated on a continuous basis to compensate for inflation and value.

These types of arrangements are generally financially safe for providers as they offer limited downside risk; however, no opportunity exists for upside or financial gains. And practices could also be subject to downside risk they are not aware of. As already discussed, MCOs can offer modified reimbursement for specific services within fee-for-service contracts. For example, purchasing items such as immunizations, chemotherapeutic agents, biologicals, intrauterine devices, etc. are all hard costs for a practice.

Practices need to be mindful of what their acquisition/administrative costs are as compared to the contractual reimbursement from each MCO. Obviously it is not in the practice's best interest to provide healthcare at a loss; too frequently practices miss this important detail and fail to properly manage this critical business process. Additionally, costs can fluctuate during the term of a contract (e.g., vaccine pricing), so reimbursement rates relative to costs must be monitored on a continuous basis.

The majority of large MCOs provide resource tools via their websites to identify payment methods and reimbursement based on the provider's Federal Tax Identification Number. In addition to fee schedule look-up tools, MCO websites provide resources such as administrative policies and procedures and reimbursement guidelines. Claim logic edits may often be found under reimbursement guidelines or claim edits. These are very important considerations as managing these details can have significant impact on the overall reimbursement for a given contract. An example of this type of impact is reduction in reimbursement for multiple surgeries. This occurs when multiple surgeries or procedures are performed by a single physician or physicians in the same group practice on the same patient during the same operative session, resulting in a possible reimbursement reduction for secondary and subsequent procedures. There are many other edit logic examples that can impact overall reimbursement for a given contract, and new methodologies can be introduced during the term of a given contract. The onus is on the practice to monitor these types of changes through MCO websites and news flashes. Reductions that occur in this manner impact overall contract performance and are an important consideration in negotiations.

All professional and facility services are billed separately and always retrospectively. This means that the physician bills for professional services and other entities submit claims for other components of the service provided after they are provided. For example, in a traditional fee-for-service arrangement, if a patient has a knee replacement the following providers may submit bills for services: orthopedic surgeon, anesthesiologist, hospital, rehabilitation, DME, home health and more. Claims are submitted during the course of care after services and/or equipment is provided. Claims are adjudicated by the MCO in the order received and payments are made in accordance with the corresponding contractual arrangements (or processed as out-of-network) and benefit design. Claims are paid or denied and this is communicated to providers and patients via an Explanation of Benefits (EOB).

Adding to its simplicity, fee-for-service reimbursement requires minimal data analytics capabilities. Practices load the fee schedule into their practice management system and automatically reconcile reimbursement rates with contract allowables (so long as rates are loaded by CPT code). Monitoring claim edit logic is critical and this can be accomplished either through electronic or manual monitoring.

As markets evolve in terms of narrow networks, patient liability, and etc., it will also become important to monitor referral patterns. While these will not impact the reimbursement rate at the micro-level, the volume aspect of the contract will impact a practice's overall revenue stream. Aside from renegotiations, monitoring these pieces is essential for proper data analytics.

Administrative and clinical integration is not required; providers are not overtly penalized for quality outcomes, cost efficiency or total cost of care. As discussed, through transparency initiatives and patient liability increases, providers that are high utilizers and/or have higher costs are impacted by patient steerage. Even with a fee-for-service agreement, patients are becoming more engaged. Engaged patients are incentivized to seek low cost providers, which ultimately impacts a practice in terms of volume.

Fundamental Drivers

Fee-for-service arrangements are shaped by market forces as well as historical relationships and is currently the primary basis for most relationships in terms of managed care contracts. In order to understand the process in upcoming chapters, it is important to appreciate the primary forces that shape this methodology. The fundamental drivers of fee-for-service arrangements are:

- The more you do, the more you make
- The more highly reimbursed the code, the better to bill
- Allows for patient expansion through network participation—HMO, PPO panels
- Quality outcomes not necessarily a consideration
- Lack of accountability for total cost of care

Inherent within this methodology are the incentives to increase volume and maximize reimbursement by rendering the highest care level of service possible. In short: do more, get more. For example, a patient presenting with muscle strain could be sent to get an MRI—an excessive option from a care management perspective. Additionally, this patient could then be required to schedule a follow-up visit, when a follow-up telephone call from clinical staff could have sufficed. This is greatly simplified, but the issue is clear. As discussed in Chapter 1, this fee-for-service driver is evolving due to strong market pressures and even in these arrangements transformations are occurring.

MCOs offer a portfolio of product offerings; HMO, Point of Service (POS) and PPO products and others. These products are offered through a designated provider network. In exchange for a discount, once credentialed, participating providers have access to a defined group of patients. Many providers have reluctantly joined HMO and PPO networks to gain access to additional patients and/or to ensure their current patient base doesn't erode. Further illustrating this point, in a recent marketing survey conducted by the Advisory Board Company, when patients were asked what would most likely make them change primary care physician, the most common response was, "My current PCP no longer accepts my insurance."[3]

In the typical fee-for-service reimbursement model, quality outcomes, cost efficiency and total cost of care are not central considerations. Initially MCOs and provider groups lacked the technology to quantify quality metrics, cost efficiency and total cost of care. Over the past decade, advances in technology and infrastructure have allowed MCOs and provider groups to aggregate data. Through such data analytics, it is possible to determine adherence to quality metrics, cost efficiency and total cost of care at the individual provider level. MCOs are sharing the information with employers and patients, often utilizing the information to develop narrow networks that steer patients to providers who have demonstrated quality and cost efficiency.

---

3 "What Drives Consumer Loyalty to a Primary Care Physician?" Advisory Board. Accessed September 21, 2016. https://www.advisory.com/research/market-innovation-center/expert-insights/2015/what-drives-consumer-loyalty-to-a-primary-care-physician

Negotiation Considerations

Although fee-for-service reimbursement models are fairly simple, straightforward and easy to administer, contracting considerations exist and should not be ignored—the devil is always in the details. When reviewing an agreement, a practice may want to pay particular attention to the key considerations in the table below:

Figure 8.3 Fee-for-Service Negotiations Key Considerations	
Key Considerations	**Practice Goal**
What products are included in the agreement? Are any excluded?	Identify what products are included in the agreement and if/how new products will be added to the contract.
How many covered lives are there relative to each product?	Determine how many lives are associated with each product in order to evaluate the impact of varying fee schedules (as applicable).
What fee schedules are included in the agreement and which products are they tied to?	Relative to product, understand if there are multiple fee schedules to consider and if so, how they are administered.
What type of reimbursement methodology does the payer utilize? Is it based on a year of Medicare? UCR? Discount off Charges? Does it blend various approaches?	Understand how reimbursement will be determined. If you have a rolling year of Medicare, identify when the new year rates will become effective
What will you be paid specifically for each service provided?	Obtain a full fee schedule and understand what is stagnant and what is fluid in terms of potential rate variation.
Are there any discounts for mid-level providers? If so, how much?	Determine if there is a multiplier for mid-level providers.
If you bill for services that do not have a standard payment methodology (also known as individually considered services), how will these be reimbursed?	Understand how reimbursement will be determined (i.e., range of reimbursement, paperwork required) if it will not be based on the fee schedule or defined 'other' source.

continued

Key Considerations	Practice Goal
If you bill for services that do not have a standard payment methodology (also known as individually considered services), how will these be reimbursed?	Understand how reimbursement will be determined (i.e., range of reimbursement, paperwork required) if it will not be based on the fee schedule or defined 'other' source.
How are new CPT codes added to the fee schedule in terms of timing and how is reimbursement determined?	Identify the methodology for payment for new CPT codes including how and when they are added by the MCO.
How are fixed costs reimbursed such as immunizations, chemotherapeutic agents, biologicals, supplies etc.?	Understand how these types of items are reimbursed and if they are revised during the contract term when the updates occur. Additionally, determine if reimbursement is below cost if revisions may be made during the course of the agreement regardless of contract term.
Who has authority to amend the agreement and how does timing/notification work?	Determine when and how your agreement can be amended. It is favorable for both parties to agree in writing prior to amending the agreement. It is not favorable for the MCO to have unilateral amendment power as this gives the MCO the authority to change the agreement without consent of the provider. These types of arrangements should only be applicable when changes are mandated by law.
Who has the authority to revise reimbursement terms?	Identify if and when reimbursement rates can be revised. It is favorable for the practice to have the ultimate say regarding any alterations to the fee schedule.
What is the required time period for notices to be given for changes to the reimbursement terms?	Understand the timing for notifications of fee schedule changes. Many times MCOs will notify a provider of a fee schedule change and the provider may have only 30 days to respond to the change before the new fee schedule becomes effective. If this is your circumstance, lengthen this timeline if at all possible.
What happens to reimbursement when the MCO initially verified eligibility but subsequent to service being provided the patient was determined not to be eligible at the time of service?	Determine how the eligibility process and retro determination are made by the MCO. Understand what mechanisms are in place for provider recourse.

continued

Key Considerations	Practice Goal
In what time period must claims be submitted?	Understand how long you have from the date of service to submit a claim before it will deny for timely filing. 180 days is most common.
Does the agreement allow for monetary "re-coups" and if yes, what is the process?	Identify in what circumstances and time periods monies can be recovered and how it will be retrieved. Many contracts allow for automatic deductions from payments which could be administratively burdensome for the practice. It is optimum to have the recoup time period consistent with the claim submission timeline. At a minimum make sure that the time parameter is defined.
Is billing for non-covered services addressed and if so, what are the requirements?	Determine the MCO requirements around notification for payment for non-covered services. Written consent from the patient is a common requirement.
What are you allowed to collect at the time of service, copayments, deductibles, coinsurance?	Understand if there are any constraints on time of service collection opportunities. Some payers set thresholds for collecting deposits and this could impede a practice's ability to effectively collect patient portions. It is favorable to not have restrictions on the collection of patient liability portions.
What is the term of the agreement and when does it renew?	Identify when the contract is effective and when the contract will end. Many agreements are 'evergreen' and will renew year after year unless terminated by either party. Other agreements lock a provider in for multiple years.
Who may terminate the agreement and what is the process and time frames?	Contracts can be terminated with and without cause. With cause would be for breach of the contract and without means that the agreement can end for any reason. It is optimum for the provider to be able to terminate the agreement at any time during the term of the agreement. It is critical for the provider to understand when and how an agreement can be terminated as part of the contracting process.

continued

Key Considerations	Practice Goal
Is there a definition for a "clean claim"?	Understand what the MCO's definition of a clean claim is and ensure that the practice is able to meet such requirements.
Is there a policy and procedure manual? How is it updated?	Evaluate the policy and procedure manual, particularly if it is a new agreement, and make sure that your practice can live with the programs. Understand how updates are communicated and make sure that you identify someone in the practice to 'own' keeping current on MCO updates.
Do timely payment parameters for the MCO exist and if yes what are the time parameters?	Determine if your state has a prompt payment regulation and make sure that the MCO abides by this legislation. It is optimum for the payer to pay claims within a reasonable timeframe (i.e., 30 days from receipt of clean claim).
Does a claim appeal process exist and if yes what is it and what are the time parameters?	Understand how you can appeal a denied claim including documentation required, time period considerations and other process considerations.
What services are excluded from the agreement?	Identify all excluded services and also determine if and how a MCO can revise the list. It is important to understand what is in/out of your purview before concluding negotiations.
Are there any network panel referral considerations to be aware of?	Determine if there are any penalties for referring outside of the MCO panel and if so how this works. It is optimum to not have any penalties relative to referral patterns as the MCO panel composition is constantly changing.
What are the provider's obligations for notifying the MCO of changes (i.e., new providers, locations)?	Understand the timeframe required for notification of provider additions/subtractions. It is optimum to have a reasonable time period (i.e., 60 - 90 days) to update MCOs regarding changes.

Additionally, be mindful of timing. Some payers are notorious for dragging negotiations out for extended periods of time. Although infrequent, with some payers, negotiations begin once termination has been issued. While this is not optimal, it is sometimes the only way to effectively proceed. Careful consideration should be made prior to evoking termination without cause; no idle threats.

Practices should have a clear understanding of impact to revenue prior to issuing termination. The first step in evaluating the timeline for a fee-for-service negotiation is identifying when the agreement can be terminated and backing up to at least six months prior to when termination must be issued. During this time period, contract terms and financial implications can be evaluated and negotiated. Contract strategy will be more thoroughly addressed in Chapter 13.

Financial Scenario Implications

Regardless of reimbursement methodology, all contracting arrangements require ongoing monitoring. In order to understand how to most effectively manage these contract types, we will start with defining key considerations when entering in to a typical fee-for-service arrangement:

- Define what CPT codes drive the most revenue by developing a Top Code list.
- Determine which fee schedules are in play and how they connect to MCO products.
- Understand how volume variances impact contract performance.
- Assess contract disposition by comparing current reimbursement rates across similar payers.
- Determine and monitor cost for services and drugs/supplies.
- Define how payer edits impact overall financial performance.
- Identify any new service offerings that could impact contract performance.

The chart on the next page represents a high-level fee-for-service analysis:

Figure 8.4 High Level Fee-for Service Analysis

CPT	Description	Contracted Rate Payer A	Medicare	%Mcare	Total Volume	Est Total Payment = Rate*Vol	Est Total Medicare Payment = Mcare * Vol
99213	Office Visit	$75	$70	107%	5,000	$375,000	$350,000
69210	Ear Wax Removal	$65	$50	130%	500	$32,500	$25,000
90471	Immunization admin	$20	$25	80%	500	$10,000	$12,500
83036	Glycosylated hemoglobin test	$8	$15	53%	500	$4,000	$7,500
Totals						$421,500	$395,000
Fee for Service Aggregate Equivalency						107%	

Through comparing managed-care contracts in aggregate, an overall equivalency can be determined. In this case, the blended Medicare rate for this contract is 107 percent. The initial step necessary in initiating this type of analysis is to identify what service offerings drive at least 80 percent to 90 percent of practice revenue. This is accomplished by identifying revenue by CPT codes and applicable modifiers plus volumes for a given time period by payer and/or product fee schedule. Once this list is compiled, contract rates are compared to current year Medicare considering volumes and the aggregate rate is determined. Once this has been completed, further analysis can reveal factors that contribute to financial performance, such as cost to provide care and MCO edit systems.

Cost to provide care can be derived in a number of ways. For example, some practices view this in terms of provider time, others calculate costs based on wRVU or in terms of visits. For simplicity, we will view cost based on visit, since volume is a primary driver for this type of methodology. Below is an example of how this calculation could work:

Figure 8.5 Cost/Visit Analysis

Total Expense	$ 650,000
Total Visits	12,500
Cost/Visit	$ 52.00

Take the practice total expense and divide by the number of visits to obtain cost per visit. For drugs, vaccines and other tangibles, the cost could be represented by **acquisition cost** plus **management cost** (typically 5 percent - 10 percent) for storage and inventory management. Cost should be factored in when constructing a negotiation and/or renegotiation strategy, which will be further discussed in Chapter 13.

Regarding edit impact, a similar calculation can assist in understanding how this logic can financially affect a practice. Below are two payers with identical volumes each impacting the practice differently with regard to overall revenue stream:

Figure 8.6 Revenue/Visit Analysis	
Total Revenue Payer 1	$ 1,000,000
Total Visits	12,500
Revenue/Visit	$80.00
Total Revenue Payer 2	$900,000
Total Visits	12,500
Revenue/Visit	$ 72.00

In these scenarios it is necessary to compare fee-for-service equivalencies to identify if there are variances in overall aggregate expected outcomes. If these are similar (for purposes of this example we will say they are both at 107 percent aggregate), then the edit logic is diminishing contract performance. Again, this can be factored in when developing a contracting strategy.

When preparing a proposal for a negotiation, it is important to consider the following:

- Identify CPT codes that fall below cost.
- Determine when comparing payer to payer if top CPT code groups fall above or below your aggregate performance.
- Understand the fee schedule methodology utilized by the payer.

If a CPT code falls below your practice cost, this information can be relayed to the payer during the negotiation process. In the case of supplies, drugs and vaccines invoices can be provided to substantiate the request and can be an effective strategy to deploy. Regarding CPT reimbursement trending, at times payers can have less than optimum fee schedules in selected areas (i.e., Evaluation and Management (E&M) codes) and these ranges can become the focal point for discussions pursuing fee schedule increases.

Payers may offer increases for services that are not high volume for your practice, so it is critical to focus on the specific high-volume CPT codes that will lead to a positive financial net result. Have a clear understanding of the fee schedule methodology being utilized by the payer currently. For example, a payer may be using 2014 Medicare PFS as a basis for their fee schedules. Providing a re-negotiation request based on 2014 Medicare PFS may be more efficient than using the most current Medicare PFS. Make it as easy as possible for everyone involved in order to expedite the negotiation timeline.

Tying key attributes, fundamental drivers, negotiation considerations and financial scenario implications together form the baseline for all contracting methodologies. While volume considerations are key in fee-for-service, other factors such as aggregation of a fee for-for-service equivalancy, payer edits and resource allocation to administer the agreement impact contract performance. High-performing practices establish resource tools such as the sample quick reference guide below to assist in monitoring and managing managed care agreements. Prudent practices will continue to dedicate resources to the evaluation of fee-for-service contractual arrangements while ramping up on alternative value base models.

Figure 8.7 Sample Contract Quick Reference Guide

Health Plan: Payer A

Contact Name	
Email	
Contact phone #	
Address	

Key Subject	Contract Term	Comments
Product Type		
Effective Date		
Percentage of Business		
Percentage of RBRVS		
Physical Therapy Fee Schedule		
MRI Fee Schedule		
Renewal Terms		
Renegotiation Window		
Termination Notification		
Amendment Process		
Timely Filing		
Recoups		
Claim Dispute Limitations		
Fee Schedule Type		
Geographic Adjustment		
New CPT Codes		
Co-Payment		

Adjustments	Reimbursement Rate	Comments
First Assist/PA considerations		
Laboratory		
Global period		
Supplies		
Medications		

Additional Information		
Provider Manual		
Formulary		
Incentive Programs		
Hospital Contract		
Excluded Services		

Chapter 9

Pay-for-Performance

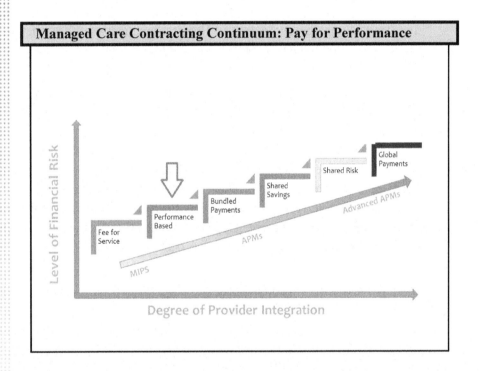

Managed Care Contracting Continuum: Pay for Performance

Pay-for-performance (P4P) contracts are transformative because they represent a shift in reimbursement methodology from simply reimbursing providers fee-for-service to rewarding value. The fee-for-service reimbursement system is designed to pay providers, separately, for the services relating to care for individual patients regardless of cost and quality. The aim in P4P's transformative methodology is to better align payers/providers with objectives (e.g., Triple Aim) in order to improve health outcomes and lower health care costs. Instead of paying for more regardless of resource and setting considerations, practices will be paid for overall value. The economic impact of transitioning fee-for-service contracts to P4P contracts is expected to be significant. UnitedHealthcare touts to employers: "We expect the aggregated return-on-investment of our value-based contracting programs to exceed 2:1 in terms of savings vs. incentives paid because only a portion of the savings will be shared with providers."[1] And CareFirst's (BCBS of Maryland) Outcome Incentive Award program (OIA), from 2011 - 2014 cited the following:

> There has been a dramatic slowing in the rise of overall costs driven by improved quality. This "bend of trend" (down to 2%) exceeds expectations and is most pronounced in the PCMH population. A key reason for the decline has been an unprecedented drop in Hospital Inpatient use (20%) beyond national trends and tightened control over drug costs—both of which have been achieved through Care Coordination.[2]

And there are countless other examples like these that exist in various payer programs across the country. In fact, the CareFirst Outcome Incentive Awards (OIA) program had a foundation that was global in nature, keeping many program attributes consistent with the CMS Medicare fee-for-service methodologies in terms of rules and incentives. So crafting commercial arrangements largely consistent with what will become the largest shared-risk program in the country (MACRA, MIPS and/or Advanced APMs program) will profoundly benefit a practice from an administrative burden perspective. If a practice is focusing on cost/quality in the MIPS program, this work can also translate effectively to a commercial contract.

On April 16, 2015, the Medicare Access and CHIP Reauthorization Act (MACRA) was signed into law, which repealed the flawed Medicare Sustainable Growth Rate (SGR) formula and created a new framework called the Quality Payment Program that will reward healthcare providers for giving better and not just more care (through MIPS and Advanced APM pathways). Medicare will no longer base annual reimbursement updates on inflation-based formulas and the transition period, from 2015 through 2019, will provide for stable, underlying annual Medicare Part B fee schedule updates through the Quality Payment Program. This increase was 0.5 percent as of July 1, 2015, and will continue through December 31, 2019. Physician Fee Schedule base rates in 2019 will be flat through 2025, while Eligible Clinicians (ECs) will have the opportunity to receive payment adjustments through MIPS or a financial incentive for participa-

---

1 UnitedHealthcare. "Shifting from Fee-for-Service to Value-Based Contracting Model," accessed August 4, 2016, http://consultant.uhc.com/assets/vbc_overview_flier.pdf
2 CareFirst. "2014 PCMH Program Performance Report," accessed August 4, 2016, https://member.carefirst.com/carefirst-resources/pdf/pcmh-program-performance-report-2014.pdf.

tion in an Advanced APM. Beginning in 2026, EC participating in an Advanced APM will receive a 0.75 percent annual update to base Medicare Part B payments, while those who do not participate in Advanced APMs will receive 0.25 percent.[3] Practices participating in Advanced APMs for a significant portion of their population will not be formally subject to the MIPS program requirements. Practices will have to make a choice to determine their future Medicare reimbursement—choices include MIPS or Advanced APM, or a practice could also partially qualify as an Advanced APM, which can have a positive impact of MIPS scoring, or the practice could opt out of MIPS if certain thresholds are reached.

The MIPS program will blend the Physician Quality Reporting System (PQRS), Value-Based Payment Modifier (VM) and Meaningful Use (MU) programs in 2019. There are four central categories in the MIPS program each with varying weights:

Category 1 Quality (weight 50 percent 2019 – 30 percent 2021+): Quality will consist of current PQRS measures and additional measures that will be solicited by the Secretary of Health and Human Services from professional organizations. Each year, the Secretary will publish a list of quality measures (available each November) to be used in the forthcoming MIPS performance period. ECs will select what measures (over 200+) to report and be assessed on. Key focus areas will include:

- Clinical care
- Safety
- Care coordination
- Patient and caregiver experience
- Population health and prevention

Category 2 Cost (weight 10 percent 2019 – 30 percent 2021+): Cost or resource use will include most measures employed in the current VM program with additional episode measures. This category will allow ECs to report their specific role in treating the beneficiary and will work to improve risk-adjustment methodologies to ensure that ECs are not penalized for serving sicker populations. Key focus areas will include:

- Per capita costs
- Medicare Spending Per Beneficiary (MSPB)

---

3 MGMA. "SGR Repealed: Looking Ahead," accessed August 4, 2016, available to MGMA members at http://www.mgma.com/practice-resources/mgma-connection-plus/mgma-connection/2015/may-2015/sgr-repealed-looking-ahead

- Episode-based measures

Category 3 Advancing Care Information (weight 25 percent stable): Advancing Care Information (previously known as Meaningful Use) will be based on electronic health record (EHR) meaningful use requirements. There are six key objectives that are evaluated on a point system, including the following:

- Protect patient information

- Patient electronic access

- Coordination of care through patient engagement

- E prescribing

- Health information exchange

- Public health and clinical data registry

The scoring mechanism weights the objectives (some more than others) to determine performance in this measure category.

Category 4 Clinical Practice Improvement Activities (weight 15 percent stable): Clinical practice improvement activities will assess ECs on their efforts to engage in the activities below. ECs will be given credit for working to improve their practices and facilitate future participation in Advanced APMs. These activities must include:

- Expanded practice access

- Population management

- Care coordination

- Beneficiary engagement

- Patient safety and practice assessment

- Participation in alternative payment models"[4]

ECs will receive a composite performance score of zero to 100 based on their performance in each of the four categories according to classification weight. Each EC's composite score will be compared to a performance threshold that consists of the average of the composite performance scores for all MIPS ECs during a period prior to the performance period. ECs whose composite performance scores are above the threshold will receive a positive payment adjustment; those whose scores fall below will receive a penalty and if the composite

---

4 Ibid

performance score is at the threshold, the EC will not receive a MIPS payment adjustment.

In terms of the current rule, this financial impact would be -/+9 percent from 2019 – 2024 but an additional $500 million per year will be available during this time period to reward top performing providers (P4P). The money collected via penalty will be pooled and CMS will distribute it to providers whose performance score exceeds the performance threshold, in a linear fashion such that those with the highest scores will theoretically capture the maximum financial incentives. It is estimated that practices could receive over 127 percent of Medicare in the top tiers (exceeding the 25th percentile), which could surpass commercial contract rates.

Advanced APMs require providers to "bear more than nominal financial risk"[5] through participation in payment models that reward attributes above and beyond volume. Based on the proposed MACRA rule, we have some further clarification regarding the definition of more than nominal risk:

> *Total Risk* – minimum 4 percent of Advanced APM spending target

> *Marginal Risk* – minimum 30 percent spending above Advanced APM target for which the Advanced APM Entity is responsible

> *Minimum Loss Rate* – maximum 4 percent of the amount by which spending can exceed the Advanced APM benchmark before the Advanced APM Entity has responsibility for losses.

Additionally, Advanced APMs must base payments on quality measures comparable to those used in the MIPS quality performance category and requires participants to use certified EHR technology.[6]

Many of the aspects of Advanced APMs are also components of categories in the MIPS program as many of the "outcomes" and "focus areas" are quite similar (i.e., patient access). With Advanced APMs, providers share in more of the risk relative to achieving goals and are therefore potentially rewarded with greater financial incentives for participation in these programs. Advanced APMs include programs created by the CMS Center for Medicare and Medicaid Innovation (the CMS Innovation Center) such as:

---

5 "Quality Payment Program." Accessed September 21, 2016. https://www.cms.gov/Medicare/Quality-Initiatives-Patient-Assessment-Instruments/Value-Based-Programs/MACRA-MIPS-and-Advanced APMs/Quality-Payment-Program-MACRA-NPRM-slides-short-version. pdf

6 CareFirst. "2014 PCMH Program Performance Report," accessed August 4, 2016, https://member.carefirst.com/carefirst-resources/pdf/pcmh-program-performance-report-2014.pdf

- Bundled Payments Programs

- Medicare Shared Savings Program (MSSP) ACOs

- All CMS Innovation Center initiatives *except* Health Care Innovation awards

- Patient Centered Medical Homes (PCMH)

Advanced APMs in the first performance period in the Quality Payment Program include:

- Comprehensive Primary Care Plus (CPC+)

- MSSP Tracks 2 & 3 and Next Generation ACO

- Oncology Care Model Two-Sided Risk Arrangement (OCM - available 2018)

- Comprehensive ESRD Care (CEC) Model

- CJR and Cardiac Care Demonstration (rsik dependent)

There are provisions for partially qualified Advanced APMs dependent upon meeting the Medicare revenue thresholds. A full listing of CMS Innovation Center initiatives can be found at http://innovation.cms.gov/initiatives/#views=-models. Practices must have at least 25 percent of their revenue attributed in an Advanced APM in 2019 and increase it to 75 percent in 2023 onward. In terms of financial incentives, practices that participate in one of these Advanced APMs will receive a 5 percent lump sum bonus each year from 2019 – 2024 and starting in 2026 will receive an additional 0.5 percent fee schedule increase over practices participating in the MIPS program.

Two tracks will be available for professionals to qualify for the bonus incentive. The first option will be based on receiving a significant percent of Medicare revenue through an Advanced APM as already discussed; the second will be based on receiving a significant percent of Advanced APM revenue combined from Medicare and commercial payers. Early adopters who start exploring these models will be positioned for participation in Advanced APMs because commercial Advanced APM revenue may count towards the Advanced APM thresholds.

Regardless of the path elected, it is amazing to think that in just seven short years the reimbursement spread between the "best" and the "worst" among providers could approach 40 percent in the Medicare payer category. Perhaps even more important is appreciating that there is a window for obtaining credit for transforming a practice in terms of commercial payer contracts. An opportunity to seize the moment exists in terms of transforming practice activities with P4P contracting efforts. Practices that capitalize on this opportunity to align and integrate payer incentives programs, to improve clinical outcomes and the patient experience, along with improving cost efficiency, will have a significant competitive advantage.

Key Attributes

Reimbursement in P4P contracts is based on a fee-for-service methodology, but adds a component to reward quality and/or cost efficiency. On the Managed Care Contracting continuum, this is the next level in terms of payer relationships. This model is becoming a mandatory consideration in terms of Medicare, and in many states for Medicaid as well. The foundational elements of pay-for-performance contracts are:

* Fee-for-service reimbursement with mutually agreed-upon added financial incentives that tie to quality/efficiency metrics and or accreditations,

* Requires formalized process by healthcare team to ensure quality metrics and cost efficiency measures are met,

* Enhanced communication flow with payer, and

* Minimal integration.

These types of contracts will require varying degrees of attention from practices. Some commercial contracts may contain one metric to consider while others may incorporate multiple measures and/or other markers such as achievement of PCMH. These contracts can be regarded as "fee-for-service plus" arrangements, as the primary payment mechanism is still rooted in fee-for-service, but an additional incentive exists. Value-based contracts most commonly contain the following added-payment methodologies:

* A component of potential payment is tied to performance on cost-efficiency and quality performance measures and can generally increase reimbursement.

* Clinical integration payments contingent on the practice engaging in the transformative activities that alter the manner in which they deliver care, such as a PCMH.

These added incentives are commonly tied to the fee-for-service reimbursement level and increases reimbursement through various mechanisms, such as:

* Pre-determined percentage increase to base contract rates (e.g., 110 percent of Medicare moves to 115 percent)

- Added dollar amount to select CPT codes (e.g., $5 more per preventive E&M codes)

- Portion of pre allocated pool of dollars (e.g., $500 million available annually through MIPS for exceptional performers)

- Increased reimbursement for reaching selected accreditation (e.g., PCMH achieved increases level of base reimbursement by 10%)

The percentage increase is realized only if the agreed-upon goals are achieved. Typically, in pay-for performance-agreements, risk is limited to upside potential. Some examples of cost-efficiency and quality performance measures included in P4P contracts are:

- Percentage generic prescriptions,

- PCMH accreditation,

- Transition of care to more cost-effective settings (i.e., inpatient to outpatient)

- HEDIS measures – outperforming peer groups

- Electronic prescribing

- Lower readmission rates

- Ancillary provider referrals (laboratory)

- Avoidable emergency room visits

- MU measures

- Lower infection rates

Often P4P agreements may employ more than one of these measures that may have weight assigned to each measure and potentially correspond with fee schedule increases. Success in these contracts will be dependent upon transforming the practice through monitoring progress continuously, enhanced communication and overall engagement from all parties.

Practices must clearly understand their baseline performance as it relates to contract measure goals. This means providers should run reports and test baseline information to ensure the starting point is accurate and that targets are realistic and achievable. Understand that both measures and targets are negotiable. Furthermore, it is a good idea to have this information validated by the payer to the extent that is possible. In some instances, these metrics will be self-reported, meaning that the payer is dependent on the practice to provide evidence of performance, while other times a reconciliation will be necessary. This is where a formalized documented monitoring process comes into play. Practices that incorporate these types of dimensions into contracts need to stay on top of performance through measuring at predetermined intervals and reconciling before the end of the performance period. This is critical if course corrections are necessary; making those adjustments within the performance period increases the possibility of reaching predetermined goals. One example that most practices will be utilizing is the Medicare Value Modifier Program's Quality and Resource Use Reports (QRURs) that are made available to providers on a semiannual basis.

Practices can download the data (https://portal.cms.gov/) and validate that providers are linked correctly, that members attributed to their practices are accurate and also understand how they are performing compared to peer groups. By reviewing this information and comparing it to practice information, providers have an opportunity to inquire if there is an issue (e.g., provider associated to the Tax Identification Number is not valid) and also measure their performance status. Without this type of rigorous data review and payer communication, value-based contracting efforts may result in less than favorable outcomes for all involved. A best practice relative to commercial payer relationships is to create standing interim progress meetings where the practice and the payer can share and validate progress. The more frequent the touch points, the better the relationship as both parties are forced to prepare for the information exchange which will enhance clarity and uncover issues before the performance period ends.

Compared to other Advanced APMs (e.g., Bundled Payment Programs, ACOs), integration requirements are minimal. While it is essential to identify a baseline and monitor performance, practices are not traditionally sharing information across the continuum of care. For example, if a practice is moving care from an inpatient to an outpatient setting, no announcement need be made externally about this transition. The practice internally revises workflows, protocols and information exchange and monitors for compliance. Care coordination teams are involved in these transitions and must become very attuned to the nuances that can impact performance. For example, one of the most effective factors for CareFirst best performers was a change in referral patterns.[7] These modifications/results need to be communicated clearly to the staff members involved in those workflows.

---

7 Machlin, S. R. Expenses for a Hospital Emergency Room Visit, 2003. Statistical Brief #111. January 2006. Agency for Healthcare Research and Quality, Rockville, Md Available at https://meps.ahrq.gov/data_files/publications/st111/stat111.pdf accessed August 4, 2016.

Additionally, changes to EMRs and/or other practice management tools are necessary to support change management activities. Often, to practice leadership's surprise, patient referrals are based on ease of referral to a facility and/or provider. It is important to get all the way to the root of the workflow to ensure that everyone is compliant and properly instructed. Furthermore, sharing performance results with staff is important. The degree of P4P contract success is dependent upon the engagement of the entire healthcare team.

Fundamental Drivers

The P4P contract's primary concepts are rooted in fairly clear fundamental drivers based on increasing quality and lowering costs. The agreements incorporate, through various mechanisms, approaches that hold the practice accountable for performance. This is in contrast to fee-for-service arrangements where there are essentially no overt financial consequences for lower quality and/or higher cost care. In traditional fee-for-service contracts, payers attempt to penalize out-of-the-norm utilization through multiple means, such as: claim adjudication edits, narrow networks, and reimbursement caps. The key drivers in P4P arrangements remain consistent with the Triple Aim and are as follows:

- Rewarding high quality/cost effective practices.

- Incorporating goals that drive efficiency and quality improvements.

- Establishing accountability between payer and provider for cost and quality of care.

- Designing quality-improvement goals that may grow volume while reducing costs.

- Providing for patient expansion through network participation—HMO, PPO and narrow network panels.

Pay-for-performance contracts reward providers for meeting established metrics that support high quality/low cost care. For example, a pediatric practice may agree to incorporate a measure into their contract such as National Quality Forum measure # 69: Appropriate Treatment for Children with Upper Respiratory Infection (URI) (Fig. 9.1):

Figure 9.1 Quality Metric Example

CMS eMeasure ID	NQF #	Measure Title	Measure Description	Numerator Statement	Denominator Statement	Measure Steward	Domain
CMS154v2	0069	Appropriate Treatment for Children with Upper Respiratory Infection (URI)	Percentage of children 3 months-18 years of age who were diagnosed with upper respiratory infection (URI) and were not dispensed an antibiotic prescription on or three days after the episode.	Children without a prescription for antibiotic medication on or 3 days after the outpatient or ED visit for an upper respiratory infection	Children age 3 months to 18 years who had an outpatient or emergency department (ED) visit with a diagnosis of upper respiratory infection (URI) during the measurement period	National Committee for Quality Assurance	Efficient Use of Healthcare Resources

As part of the contracting process, the practice performance expectation parameters are established in comparison to goal. Assuming the practice's current performance relative to the target is 50 percent, the practice could work with the payer to establish a primary target (70 percent) and even a stretch target (90 percent) over a specified time period. If the practice reaches the first level of performance improvement, it is rewarded with a 1.5 percent increase to fee-for-service rates, and if the stretch target is realized, the increase jumps to 3 percent.

This can be spread over multiple years in some cases where the time necessary to implement workflows would necessitate more than a one-year timeframe. If the baseline target is not achieved, there is no increase to fee-for-service rates, or if the increase was prospective then rates would revert back to the practice's original fee schedule. The higher the quality of care, the greater the reward. This can positively impact cost of care as prescription drug costs are decreased and the group improves performance for this metric. Of course, there are usually several metrics incorporated into these types of agreements and this is a simplification. Alternatively, some agreements may establish a bonus pool in lieu of an incremental increase; access to which can be gained in incremental amounts (percentages) based on the practice's success at reaching established targets.

The measures established in pay-for-performance contracts can vary widely depending on payer administrative capabilities, practice gaps in performance and a practice's ability to measure metrics. There are many instances where what a group measures and or wishes to report on are simply not possible given a payer system architecture. Payer systems vary widely and, not unlike practice management systems, differ in functionality. Payers and providers need to reach mutual agreement on measures that are both administratively simple and efficiency and quality driven. Some payers are able to share data with practices regarding their performance compared to peer groups for a suite of measures, while others will not be as sophisticated. Payers will often only consider the types of arrangements mentioned if the practice meets a spend threshold, meaning that they comprise a claims expense worthwhile to the payer in the market.

If the payer is able to share performance information, the first step is to understand the data. The best way to examine this information is in a face-to-face meeting between payer and provider. The more that is understood about what is possible clinically, and the contingent economic implications, if any, the better the value-based contract design. It is essential that providers are totally on board with the contracting methodology and understand exactly how it will be implemented, measured and managed.

This process is the foundation for establishing accountability between the parties. As a practice analyzes data components, discusses potential metrics, evaluates potential targets, communicates timing, and reports responsibilities and financial implications, it begins to establish its foundation for accountability. Documenting important agreements along the way is vital in administering the contract. Here is a sample matrix that can be used in documenting these steps:

Figure 9.2 Pay-for-Performance Contract Matrix				
Task	Responsible Party	Completion Date	Findings	Next Step
Review payer performance reports with practice leadership				
Validate payer performance reports with practice data				
Identify potential metrics for contracts				
Craft proposal including timelines				
Meet with payer and submit proposal				
Negotiate contract financial and language implications; finalize				
Identify communication plan				
Perform interim progress review(s)				
Validate applicable increase provided				

Ensure that relevant findings and facts are shared with the practice's payer partner. If everyone starts on the same page, the better it goes. That's especially important regarding communication, as practices/payers who neglect the communication plan risk destabilizing the relationship. Being particularly vigilant in this area ensures that the practice can proactively address issues and foster a sustainable relationship.

The way a P4P contract incentivizes reducing costs and improving quality can create a double win for practices. An example of this could be a colorectal cancer screening metric:

Figure 9.3 Quality Metrics Example #2

CMS eMeasure ID	NQF #	Measure Title	Measure Description	Numerator Statement	Denominator Statement	Measure Steward	Domain
CMS130v2	0034	Colorectal Cancer Screening	Percentage of adults 50-75 years of age who had appropriate screening for colorectal cancer.	Patients with one or more screenings for colorectal cancer. Appropriate screenings are defined by any one of the following criteria below: - Fecal occult blood test (FOBT) during the measurement period - Flexible sigmoidoscopy during the measurement period or the four years prior to the measurement period - Colonoscopy during the measurement period or the nine years prior to the measurement period	Patients 50-75 years of age with a visit during the measurement period	National Committee for Quality Assurance	Clinical Process/ Effectiveness

In this measure, the practice is incentivized to provide appropriate screenings for adults between the ages of 50 and 75 years. By focusing on screening occurrences, the practice is driving an increase in volume of preventive services that may increase practice revenue. In many instances, these types of contracts are catalysts for establishing advanced-care teams such as care coordinators, pharmacists, practice clinical staff and others. When these teams focus collaboratively on goals/objectives, the opportunity for best performance in these arrangements is maximized.

These value-driven arrangements can drive practices into narrow networks. Best-performing practices provide high-quality care at a reasonable cost and are the natural choice for high-performing networks. By performing well in these contracts, practices expand potential patient bases as the products/networks designed by payers are typically tiered in terms of performance. Essentially, everybody who meets minimum credentialing standards are in the default network. Many payers begin to refine networks in terms of rankings and tie patient liability to steer patients into the higher performing practices. There can be several layers of tiered networks that can range from typical PPO to wide-coverage networks to employer-specific networks. The better the practice's performance in these contracts, the more access the practice will have to patients.

Negotiation Considerations

Pay-for-performance contracts build upon the framework of the fee-for-service arrangement. When assessing negotiation considerations, be sure to fold all of the fee-for-service considerations into the practice strategy and build upon that foundation. Key P4P considerations:

- Understand quality/cost efficiency metrics being measured.
- Secure baseline reports to understand starting point for each measure.
- Reach agreement on each measure, what is realistic and achievable.
- Understand the reporting process: what, when and how.
- Understand exposure for downside potential and/or withhold.
- Address timing of future financial incentives.

The first step in a P4P contract is identifying the potential quality/cost efficiency measures usable in the arrangement. There are many variations in terms of what payers offer in different markets. Understand that everything is negotiable, including measures and targets. While many payers will provide measures for consideration, others will entertain measures that providers put forth. Some payers will provide a claims expense budget that must be decreased while improving quality targets (e.g., CareFirst). A common theme with all of these arrangements is the metrics need to be measurable and be comparable to industry standards. Groups that put forth assorted home-grown measures that have no evidenced-based comparable peer data are rarely considered by payers. The first step in identifying candidates for P4P measures is to meet face-to-face with the payer. A practice can start by asking what is happening with other like specialties and build upon that framework. If no framework exists, the practice can offer the measures that it already tracks and that providers are already working on improving. At times, the increase can be tied to meeting the measure while other times the increase can be based on improvement and it really depends on where a practice performance lies on the continuum. For example, a primary care provider may be meeting Advancing Care Information criteria in the Quality Payment Program that could be rewarded in a P4P scenario. Or staying with the primary-care theme, a provider could be a Tier 3 PCMH and would have to meet multiple measures to maintain this accolade. Some of those measures could be incorporated into a P4P agreement, even if they are being met, because the group is already providing the desired level of care and the practice can be rewarded for maintaining the PCMH credential. As part of this discovery process, make sure that the practice is able to produce the reports necessary for reporting this data to the payer and obtain their sign off on the reporting mechanism. If there is a validation component on the payer side, test that as well to make sure that everyone is on the same page.

In terms of assessing the measures for the contract, make sure that the parameters are realistic. For example, a group was asked to incorporate a measure for prescribing generic medications and the payer was offering a percentage increase derived from the percentage of generics prescribed. When assessing the measure, the group identified they were already beating the national average, and concluded it was unrealistic to agree to the proposed target. Instead, they introduced an alternative measure, but without doing their homework, they could have been holding themselves to a potentially unachievable target. Consider practice goals and programs in play in order to capitalize on existing initiatives. Minimizing administrative burden for all involved should be a key focal point.

Once the measures have been identified, determine the specifics in terms of exactly what will be reported, including timeframe, documents, validation process and responsible parties on both sides. Consider creating a P4P summary workflow to outline the work streams, as seen in the following example:

Figure 9.4 Pay-for-Performance Key Element Chart

Measure	Measurement Weight	Measurement Period	Timeline for Addressing Discrepancies	% Increase	Baseline	Target	Effective Date of Increase	Practice Responsibile Party	Payer Responsible Party	Interim Performance Report Reviewed	Payer Validation Report Reviewed

By creating this type of well-defined workflow with the payer partner, the practice will have created a framework for monitoring performance. Anticipate there may be challenges (as with all new methodologies), but through defining and agreeing to a framework the practice will be better able to optimally manage the agreement. Identifying the timing for increases is key, in order to assure that the billing department monitors appropriately

Financial Scenario Implications

Evaluating financial scenarios with a P4P contract component starts with considering the foundational elements described in Chapter 8. A fee-for-service equivalency can prove to be an effective way to gauge and communicate what a P4P arrangement could/should mean to a practice. In addition to the foundational considerations, P4P contracts will require additional financial analyses, including:

- Understanding baseline in terms of current practice expense/measure/targets.

- Determining impact of increase for each measure, including weighting if applicable.

- Estimating overall savings for measures as possible.

The baseline is critical and validating this initial starting place with the payer is the first step. For example, if a P4P arrangement has a matrix methodology (that considers cost and quality interdependently), then understanding the expense attribution and quality measure score baseline will enable a practice to measure progress during the course of the performance period. In order to compare notes, select a time period for consideration and extract the relevant data points from the practice management system and/or EHR. Summarize the information and provide details (de-identified) to the payer and review payer data to determine if the information reconciles with their data.

If a P4P arrangement has multiple quality measures and each are weighted, the following table could be used as a guide:

P4P Sample Measure Progress Chart

Figure 9.5 Pay-for-Performance Measure Progress Chart						
Measure	weight	current	target	actual	increase possibility	increase actual
Patient access	25%	30%	60%	62%	1%	1%
Generic prescription	25%	50%	55%	55%	1%	1%
Patient satisfaction	25%	75%	90%	80%	1%	0%
Care setting differential	25%	0%	100%	100%	1%	1%
Total						3%

In this example, each measure has a weight and the percentage increase is attained only if the measure is achieved. The total possible increase for the performance period was 4 percent, but the practice achieved only three of the four goals, therefore the increase was 3 percent.

Understand the total value of what the practice brings to the table. For example, if a practice has extended hours, has an open-access schedule and is open every day of the year, it could be presumed that the practice is reducing visits to the emergency room (ER). The estimated average cost of an ER visit is $580 more than the cost of an office visit.[8] Given this information, a practice could develop some scenarios around what the practice is saving the payer:

Figure 9.6 Pay-for-Performance ER Visit Estimated Savings			
Payer 1 Visits Annually	2,500		
	1%	5%	10%
Estimated Savings	$ 14,500	$ 72,500	$ 145,000

Payers may be able/willing to provide information comparing the practice to its peer groups as depicted in the table below, which can be utilized in developing the value proposition.

---

8 Centers for Medicare & Medicaid Services. "Quality Payment Program: Delivery System Reform, Medicare Payment Reform, & MACRA," accessed August 4, 2016, https://www.cms.gov/Medicare/Quality-Initiatives-Patient-Assessment-Instruments/Value-Based-Programs/MACRA-MIPS-and-Advanced APMs/MACRA-MIPS-and-Advanced APMs.html

Figure 9.7 Pay-for-Performance Practice Performance Comparison			
Sample	**Practice**	**Peers**	**Variance**
	Sample Pediatrics & Adolescents	Peer Group Practices Pediatrics	Difference Between Practice and Peers
Members	3,521	185,201	
Average Age	10	9	
Average Risk Score	0.76	0.65	
Primary Care Visits*	3,903	3.680	6.1%
Specialist (Office) Visits*	2,871	2,188	31.2%
ER Visits*	98	133	-26.3%
Potentially Inappropriate ER Visits	25	45	-44.4%
Hospital Admissions*	12	12	0.0%
Urgent Care Visits*	164	209	-21.5%
Convenience Care Visits*	41	52	21.2%
MRI and CAT scans*	21	14	50%
Rx - % Generic	70.6%	73.6%	
Number of Practices		241	

*Utilization metrics reported per 1,000 members

Based on this information, the payer saved $30,000 in expense by analyzing this one measure alone. It is important to understand the economic benefit that achieving measures can have on overall expense and to discuss these points th payer partners. The goal is to share the savings in the form of an increase that rewards practice activities for increased value and cost efficiency. Below is and example of how the math works when pulling all of the attributes together, building on the fee-for-service architecture and adding the P4P component.

Figure 9.8 Pay-for-Performance Sample Contract Math

CPT	Description	Contracted Rate Payer A	Medicare	%Mcare	Total Volume	Est Total Payment = Rate*Vol	Est Total Medicare Payment = Mcare * Vol
99213	Office Visit	$75	$70	107%	5,000	$375,000	$350,000
69210	Ear Wax Removal	$65	$50	130%	500	$32,500	$25,000
90471	Immunization admin	$20	$25	80%	500	$10,000	$12,500
83036	Glycosylated hemoglobin test	$8	$15	53%	500	$4,000	$7,500
Totals						$421,500	$395,000
Fee for Service Aggregate Equivalency						107%	

	Current	Target	Actual	% Increase	Up	Actual
Generic Rx	50%	55%	55%	2%	$8,430	$8,430
Lab	10%	7%	8%	2%	$-	$-
Auto Inflator	1%					$4,215
Totals						$434,145
Fee for Service Aggregate Equivalency with PB						110%	

In this scenario, the fee-for-service aggregate equivalency without P4P measure is 107 percent. The practice had an auto inflator (which is optimum) and met one measure but missed the target on the other. The net impact is an increase of 3 percent over their current agreement. Over time, the measures may change as various opportunities will be discovered. By establishing a core approach, methodology, communication plan and monitoring program, practices can position to share the benefit of focusing on areas of improvement with payer partners and move toward achieving the Triple Aim.

Chapter 10

Bundled Payments — Episode of Care

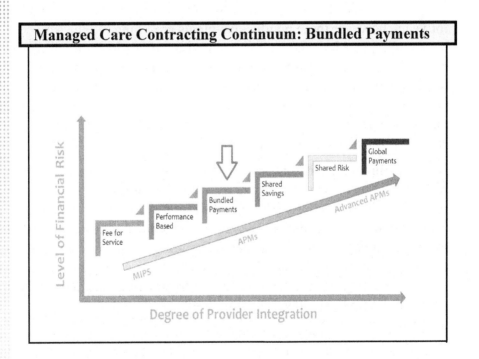

Managed Care Contracting Continuum: Bundled Payments

We all like a good deal. Good deals provide value. Consider purchasing phone, cable TV and internet service packages, or an all-inclusive trip to a destination resort. These services are often sold bundled together at one price. Consumers gravitate towards bundled services for many reasons: reputable product or service, transparent costs, ease of understanding, coordinated service and usually no additional hidden fees. Bundled payment programs are fast becoming one of the primary vehicles used within the healthcare transformation paradigm to improve quality, decrease cost and increase patient satisfaction.

Bundled payments are predetermined payments for an episode of care or a case rate for particular diagnostic condition or surgical procedure such as joint replacement. Often these services are provided by Centers of Excellence, and through the use of financial incentives, employers are steering patients to facilities and providers who have demonstrated they provide quality outcomes at a reasonable price for specific procedures.

Bundled payments are not new to the healthcare industry. Global obstetrics care and global surgical care have been reimbursed via a standard bundling model for years, however these bundled payments are limited to the services provided by a single provider. The next generation of APMs include reimbursement for multiple providers across various care settings. In the future, this APM type may be considered an Advanced APM under MACRA if providers take on more than nominal risk. Often these arrangements can include providers who are not organizationally related. Herein lies the point: bundled payments incentivize providers to coordinate care and enhance efficiency.

How has this model fared? From 1991 to 1996, Medicare experimented with seven hospitals providing a single payment to those institutions and physicians for coronary artery bypass graft (CABG) surgery, resulting in 42 million dollars saved on 10,000 procedures.[1] Savings were achieved through shorter length of stay, better pharmaceutical management and lower post-acute care cost. These episodes, or bundled payments, provided reimbursement through a single payment for a group of services related to a treatment or condition that may have involved multiple providers in multiple settings.[2]

By their nature, bundled payments are value-based; they require providers to assume some degree of financial risk for the cost of services for a particular treatment or condition, as well as costs associated with preventable complications. Today, the majority of bundled payments are made retrospectively; this payment scenario allows providers participating in the bundle to be reimbursed on a fee-for-service basis as services are provided. At the conclusion of the bundle, a **trueing up** occurs, comparing the actual cost to the agreed-upon bundled

1 Gosfield, Alice "Bundled Payment: Practicalities, Contractual and Governance Issues." Accessed October 7, 2016. https://www.healthlawyers.org/events/programs/materials/documents/mm13/tt_gosfield.pdf

2 Silversmith, J. "Five Payment Models: The Pros, the Cons, the Potential." Minnesota Medicine Magazine 94, no. 2 (February 2011): 45-48.

payment, commonly referred to as a **virtual bundle**. If the actual expense is less than the predetermined target, providers share in the savings. Conversely, if the actual expense exceeds the predetermined target, providers are responsible to repay the cost overage.

In some cases, a single payment for an episode of care may be made to one entity. This option is dependent on the scope of services that a provider delivers. For example, a gastroenterology group may be capable of providing all services necessary for endoscopy and colonoscopy procedures: the endoscopy surgical facility and professional physician services for gastroenterology, anesthesia, and pathology. The gastroenterology group controls and manages all services provided within the bundle. A single payment is made to the group and the group distributes the reimbursement through its own internal compensation mechanisms.

More commonly, multiple disparate providers across various settings are providing the services included in the bundle. The intent of this APM is to decrease healthcare spending while improving quality by creating a financial incentive for providers to eliminate services that are clinically ineffective or duplicative. "Another potential effect is to encourage coordination of care by holding multiple providers jointly accountable, through shared payment, for the cost of a bundle of services."[3]

For example, if the gastroenterology group mentioned above does not provide anesthesia and/or pathology services, they would need to work collaboratively with these providers to determine reimbursement for those portions of the bundle. This approach will require participation in new activities such as negotiating provider-to-provider for components of the bundle, relationship building, cost of care determination and benchmarking, interim reporting and so on.

In order to set the stage for commercial bundles, we will discuss the CMS initiatives, as the commercial payers frequently utilize similar methodologies. As previously mentioned in the P4P section, the ACA created the CMS Center for Medicare and Medicaid Innovation (the CMS Innovation Center). The overarching goals of the CMS Innovation Center are to:

- Improve care coordination, beneficiary experience, and accountability in a person-centered manner.

---

3 Hussey PS, Ridgely MS, Rosenthal MB. The PROMETHEUS bundled payment experiment: slow start shows problems in implementing new payment models. Health Aff (Millwood). 2011 Nov;30(11):2116-24. doi: 10.1377/hlthaff.2011.0784. PubMed PMID: 22068404.

- Support and encourage providers that are interested in continuously re-engineering care to deliver better care and better health at lower costs though continuous improvement.

- Create a cycle that leads to continually decreasing the cost of an acute or chronic episode of care while fostering quality improvement.

- Develop and test payment models that create extended accountability for better care, better health at lower costs for the full range of health care services.

- Shorten the cycle time for adoption of evidence-based care.

- Create environments that stimulate rapid development of new evidence-based knowledge.[4]

The innovation models are organized into the following seven categories:

- Accountable Care

- Episode-Based Payment Initiatives

- Primary Care Transformation

- Initiatives Focused on the Medicaid and CHIP Population

- Initiatives Focused on the Medicare-Medicaid Enrollees

- Initiatives to Accelerate the Development and Testing of New Payment and Service Delivery Models

- Initiatives to Speed the Adoption of Best Practices

Bundled payments fall under the category of Episode-Based Payment Initiatives. Under these models, healthcare providers are held accountable for the cost and quality of care beneficiaries (hospitalization and extends for a limited period of time thereafter. Bundled Payment Care Improvement (BPCI) is a voluntary program comprised of four broadly-defined models of care linking payments for multiple services for beneficiaries received during an episode of care. There are 48 episodes with each comprised of up to 15 individual Medicare Severity-Diagnosis Related Group (MS-DRG) codes for various specialties. The models are as follows:

Model 1: The episode of care is defined as the inpatient stay in an acute care hospital. CMS pays the hospital a discounted amount based on the payment rates established under the Inpatient Prospective Payment system. Physicians are re-

---

4 "Medicare Program: Bundled Payments for Care Improvement Models." February 14, 2014. https://www.gpo.gov/fdsys/pkg/FR-2014-02-14/pdf/2014-03311.pdf

imbursed separately under the Medicare Physician Fee Schedule—not included in the bundle.

Model 2: The episode includes the inpatient stay in an acute care hospital plus the post-acute care and all related services up to 90 days after hospital discharge. This includes reimbursement for physician services.

Model 3: The episode begins at initiation of post-acute care services with a skilled nursing facility, inpatient rehabilitation facility, long-term care hospital or home health care agency. This bundle includes physician services provided after the acute inpatient stay.

Model 4: The episode includes hospital and physician services where payment is made on a prospective basis encompassing all services provided by the hospital, physicians and other practitioners that occur during the inpatient stay. The hospital is responsible for distribution of the bundle payment.

There are two phases of implementation for models 2, 3 and 4.

- *Phase 1* is the initial period referred to as the preparation period where the participants prepare to assume financial risk.

- *Phase 2*, referred to as the risk bearing period, where upon execution of an agreement with CMS, the provider assumes financial liability for the episode of care.

The BPCI initiative is the most widespread of the CMS Innovation Center initiatives and was a catalyst for the Comprehensive Care for Joint Replacement (CJR) Model. This model includes 800 inpatient prospective payment hospitals within 67 metropolitan statistical areas from Los Angeles to New York. These entities will become financially responsible for the episode of care for patients admitted for a lower extremity joint replacement.

The CJR model is a five-year program with ***mandatory*** facility participation. Hospital facilities will be financially responsible for the episode of care from the admit date to 90 days from discharge including the procedure, inpatient admission and all care related to the patient's recovery. Services included and excluded in the episode of care are listed in the table below.[5]

---

5 Highlights for the proposed comprehensive care for joint replacement payment model for acute care hospitals furnishing lower extremity joint replacement services rule. August 3, 2015. Accessed September 21, 2016. http://www.apta.org/BundledModels/CCJR/Sum

CJR Services

Figure 10.1 Comprehensive Care for Joint Replacement Services	
Included Services	**Excluded Services**
Physicians' Services	Acute clinical condition not arising from existing episode-related chronic clinical condition or complications of joint replacement surgery
Inpatient hospitalization (including readmission)	Chronic conditions that are generally not affected by joint replacement surgical procedure or post-surgical care
Inpatient Psychiatric facility	
Long-Term Care Hospital (LTCH)	
Inpatient Rehabilitation Facility (IRF)	
Skilled Nursing Facility (SNF)	
Home Health Agency (HHA)	
Hospital Outpatient Services	
Outpatient Rehabilitation Services	
Clinical Laboratory Services	
Durable Medical Equipment (DME)	
Part B Drugs	
Hospice	

Hospitals and other providers contributing services within the 90-day episode of care will be paid fee-for-service under the Medicare fee schedule. CMS proposes to establish target prices for each participant hospital for each performance year and to employ a retrospective two-sided risk model. If the actual cost of the episode of care is less than the target expense and quality thresholds are met the facility is eligible to share in the savings. Conversely, if the actual cost of care exceeds the target expense the facility is responsible to repay CMS. The goals are clear: align incentives among multiple providers across multiple settings to manage and coordinate patient care thereby improving quality and decreasing cost while improving patient satisfaction.

Similar to Phase 1 of the Model, Phases 2, 3 and 4 of the BPCI Initiative, year one of the five-year CJR program is without downside risk. Starting in year two, CMS proposes that the hospital facilities must retain 50 percent of the downside risk and that the hospital may not share more than 25 percent of its repayment responsibilities with any one provider or supplier. This means that the hospitals will be incentivized to share at least 50 percent of the risk with other providers, including physicians.

It was not an accident CMS selected total joint replacements to further test the feasibility of bundled payments, as this is the most prevalent inpatient surgery for Medicare beneficiaries. The average Medicare expenditure for total hip and knee replacement ranges from $16,500 to $33,000 across the country. The expansion of bundle payments to CJR validates CMS assertions that the results from these initiatives are favorable. Furthermore, increasing care coordination results in decreased cost variation and improve outcomes. It is anticipated that future bundled payment methodologies will be expanded to encompass additional procedures, as this APM is attaining the desired results.

Key Attributes

On the managed care continuum, bundled payments are next up the ladder from P4P contracts. The level of sophistication required to successfully work within this methodology is more advanced and necessitates a moderate degree of integration, often between disparate providers who may not be organizationally related. Additionally, other key attributes include the following:

- Single retrospective or prospective predetermined payment to providers and/or healthcare facilities for all services to treat a given condition of care—also known as episode of care or **case rate**

- High volume, high expenditure, predictable procedures that have easily identifiable start and end dates and quality measures

- Moderate analytics capabilities

- Moderate integration

As previously explained in the BPCI and CJR sections, the majority of bundled payments are virtual bundles with provider and facilities being paid fee-for-service during the episode with a **trueing -up** during a defined reconciliation period after the conclusion of the episode of care. The budget for these bundles is established at a target rate based on historical performance and in many instances there is a predetermined discount to the target prices (e.g., 2 percent less than historical performance) setting the bar for increasing efficiency. When the payment is prospective, the entity facilitating the bundle receives the dollars at the start of the episode. The advantage here is that while obtaining the dollars up front improves cash flow, it does not obviate the necessity for bundle management.

Selecting high volume, high expenditure, predictable procedures requires both financial and clinical analysis. From a practice perspective, it is important to identify what will provide the biggest bang for the buck. Historically, episodes have been identified by pinpointing those procedures that have a wide variation in cost with opportunity for standardization. Here are some key questions to consider:

- What are the practice's high volume procedures (think bread & butter)?

- Which services may have high cost variation and how can the practice validate?

- What procedures lend themselves to a clear start and end date?

- What quality metrics can be measured relative to the procedure?

- Are there opportunities for enhanced care coordination for a particular procedure?

- Which procedures have a predictable package of care?

Success is more likely if a paradigm shift occurs from one based on volume to one based on value. If practices continue to operate as status quo—operating on the "more you do the more you make" model—failure is highly probable. To be successful in APMs like bundles, practices need to think in terms of teams instead of silos and "win/win" in place of "win/lose." One example of how to successfully approach bundles is to identify efficiency opportunities and eliminate low-value services that increase costs without adding value (e.g., through care coordination, ensuring that duplicate services, such as radiology, are not provided). Additionally, many contracts include quality metric components; it is key to identify what makes sense for the episode of care. In many instances, these can be consistent with quality reporting and/or HEDIS measures. These measures and improvement thresholds may be incorporated into the bundle arrangement. It is essential, as with any quality measure aspect of contracting, to establish an understandable baseline, including reporting timelines and measurement methodologies.

Depending upon the bundle, practices will need to analyze service information throughout the entire continuum of care. Analysis of service utilization, providers, facility stays, readmissions, complication rates, ancillary services, outcomes, budget variances and more will require ongoing effort. Monitoring all aspects of the bundle, with an eye to detail, will provide the care team with the necessary information to make changes to workflows and/or care plans when appropriate, evaluate referring provider trends and manage care to improve quality and increase efficiency.

A moderate degree of clinical integration is required, as coordinating care throughout the episode is critical to achieving optimum outcomes. Because collaboration is limited to the episode of care, the focus will be on intersecting around aspects of care related to the episode and not the broader population. Of course, this is the beginning of establishing relationships across the care continuum and ultimately may impact broader care management activities. Communication is fundamental to managing this methodology, as success is highly dependent upon collaboration.

For example, in managing care provided in the post-acute setting, outcomes/efficiency will vary by facility, and providers need to be kept informed in order to revise referral patterns as needed. "MedPAC analysis shows that nearly 14 percent of Medicare patients that are discharged from a hospital to a SNF are readmitted to the hospital for conditions that could have been avoided."[6] It is critical to understand partner performance in bundled payment programs and much of this data (e.g., Star Ratings) is publicly available. Better performing practices constantly monitor performance/ratings and link analysis with impactful communication to stakeholders.

Fundamental Drivers

Healthcare reform has relegated the word volume to mean something unfavorable, however, in bundled payments, volume is favorable and necessary. When managed appropriately and efficiently, volume is essential to the success of bundled payments. Volume allows providers to reduce input costs and maximize growth based on total cases.

The summarized fundamental drivers for successful bundled payments are as follows;

- Collaboration to improve efficiency and quality

---

6 "Post-Acute Care in the Medicare Program." Post-Acute Care in the Medicare Program. June 14, 2013. Accessed October 06, 2016. http://www.hhs.gov/asl/testify/2013/06/4481.html

- Mutual accountability between multiple providers

- Volume-reducing input costs and growing total number of cases

Unlike fee-for-volume, bundled payments have several unique fundamental drivers. The primary goal is to demonstrate how your practice and the collective care partners are experts at providing the services within the bundle. Like a seasoned relay team, provider care partners collectively establish a mutually accountable team to evaluate each service and process provided within the bundle, including patient transitions between health care settings. The care team must evaluate protocols to ensure processes are based on scientific evidence, develop and refine policies and procedures, eliminate low value, high cost inefficient services and ensure patient transfers between providers and care settings are coordinated and that care is provided in a patient-centric manner.

As an example, a three-day post-operative patient contacted their nurse case manager, stating, "I have sprung a leak." The nurse case manager requested the patient visit the outpatient clinic setting. She evaluated the surgical site, determining the drainage was to be expected and it warranted no further action. She reviewed the post-operative care plan with the patient and provided reassurance. In the past, the patient would have struggled to reach a nurse and most likely would have ended up in the ER. This interaction demonstrates the Triple Aim in play: the care occurred in the right setting, at a lower cost and resulted in high patient satisfaction.

Frequently, providers interpret bundled payments as being paid less for services provided. "It is not about working harder or cheaper; it is about reducing complications, readmissions and gaps in care."[7] Don't be fooled: care redesign is not easy. It takes work to re-engineer established processes. It is common initially to experience a reduction in overall reimbursement primarily driven by lower production. However, over time, this will be offset by increased efficiencies and volume. The focus needs to be on doing more of what you are best at delivering to maximize the benefits.

Negotiation Considerations

Similar to all value-based payment methodologies, bundled payment arrangements contain some degree of inherent risk. "Bundled payment, properly constructed, gives the providers medical management risk- the risk of making good

---

7 The Bundled Payment Guide for Physicians. Accessed September 21, 2016. http://www.accc-cancer.org/ ossn_network/NC/pdf/TAC-Bundled-Payment-Guide.pdf

medical decisions within the payment boundaries."[8] In addition to the common negotiation considerations included in all value-based payment arrangements (cost efficiency, quality measures and risk adjustments), bundled payments also include additional critical key elements. These key elements may be organized into three categories:

- Administrative
- Quality
- Financial considerations

The critical question is: Who holds the bundle? This is not an easy question to answer. It may be best addressed by determining who is best equipped to hold the bundle; it may be a hospital or it may be a physician group. Ideally, care partners evaluate each entity's stake and determine what value-added services they bring to the negotiation table. Regardless of who holds the bundle, if a singular payment is made, an appropriation of funds to each participating care partner will need to occur. If payment is made via a virtual payment, reconciliation will need to occur on an ongoing basis.

Clearly define all services to be included and/or excluded in the bundle including but not limited to: narrative description an accompanying CPT, Healthcare Common Procedure Coding System (HCPCS), ASA Physical Status Classification System (ASA PS), DRG codes, etc. Include site of service settings such as skilled nursing, inpatient rehabilitation facilities, outpatient rehabilitation services and durable medical equipment. Specific start and end dates should be outlined within the agreement.

For example, care and services provided three days prior to the procedure(s) and care and services included 90 consecutive days thereafter. If multiple care partners are providing services within the bundle, delineate who is providing what service as well as each care partner's designated role. Also, determine who will be responsible for managing the reporting/analysis aspects of the arrangement, including timelines and communication protocols. The primary goal is to provide clarity thereby removing any possibility for ambiguity in managing the bundle.

The methodology for selecting, developing and managing quality metrics and patient satisfaction for bundled payment arrangements are similar to the processes employed in P4P arrangements. Bundled payments differ from P4P in that

---

8 What's Fair In Bundled Payment Contracting? Managed Care Magazine Online. 2016. Accessed September 21, 2016. http://www.managedcaremag.com/archives/2013/10/whats-fair-bundled-payment-contracting

they require a high degree of collaboration between multiple and often disparate care partners. The entire care team needs to reach agreement and be on the same page regarding the selection of the quality measures, determining baseline measurements and establishing target thresholds.

Financial Considerations

The financial considerations for bundle payments require specificity and clarity. Practices need to clearly delineate the financial assumptions. Most commonly, bundled payments are based on retrospective claim analysis: what was paid in the past for all services provided in the bundle. The big questions are: how should a bundle price be developed and how should the funds be appropriated? In order to set the bundle price, the team delivering the bundle needs to evaluate the resources/costs necessary to deliver the care. The challenge has been that much of this information has not been available historically, and as a result practices have had limited insight into costs outside of their practice.

Good news: Big Data is available to practices through CMS' VM program found in the Medicare QRUR data, Healthcare Bluebook, Medicare Provider Utilization and Payment Data, payer websites and many other transparency tools. Care partners can collaborate and use this information to determine possible bundle pricing. Additionally, evaluating this information to understand the "spend" for each component is a starting point when identifying fund appropriation scenarios. If utilizing data for Medicare beneficiaries (QRUR), attribute costs based on percentage as available in the spend categories to estimate bundle appropriations.

On the following page is an example methodology for pulling together pricing for a gastrointestinal (GI) bundle:

Figure 10.2 Gastrointestinal Bundle Example

CPT	Description	Contracted Rate Payer A	Medicare	%Mcare	Total Volume	Est Total Payment = Rate*Vol	Est Total Medicare Payment = Mcare * Vol
PROFESSIONAL							
45378	Colonoscopy	$450	$300	150%	250	$112,500	$75,000
88306	Pathology	$50	$40	125%	250	$12,500	$10,000
00810	Anesthesia	$200	$150	133%	250	$50,000	$37,500
Facility	Surgery	$575	$400	144%	250	$143,750	$100,000
Totals		$1,275				$318,750	$222,500
Fee for Service Aggregate Equivalency						143%	
Bundle		$1,350			250	$337,500	$222,500
Fee for Service Aggregate Equivalency						152%	

In this scenario, the fee-for-service aggregate equivalency without the bundle is 143 percent. The practice priced the bundle $75 higher than the estimate costs in total. The net impact is an increase to 152 percent in terms of aggregate fee-for-service equivalency. For a retrospective payment, the overage would be distributed to providers. The distribution of proceeds and/or recoveries should be outlined ahead of time in order to clarify roles/responsibilities and potential financial impact. The contract should clearly outline these gainsharing opportunities as well as repayment parameters. There are many ways to determine how to split these responsibilities: by cost of care compared to the episode total cost, performance relative to quality metric targets or a weight of these and/or other measures.

Practices should ensure the contract document includes language addressing how outliers will be identified as well as what justifies breaking a bundle or excluding the patient from the bundle, including, but not limited to: comorbidities, extended length of stay, health events unrelated to the primary procedure, catastrophic costs (e.g., cases exceeding $50,000+). For example, a patient was admitted for a total knee replacement, subsequent to the procedure it was determined the patient had stage-four cervical cancer. The bundle was broken, and the patient was excluded from the payment methodology due to the fact the patient experienced an unrelated health event, cancer.

Regardless if the bundle payment is made to one entity or if a payment is made to multiple providers via a virtual bundle, the financial reconciliation processes should be outlined clearly. Bundled payments are based on the average per-patient cost of care, however, for a myriad of reasons, not all patients are average and risk adjustment considerations should be addressed and well understood. Additionally, consideration should be given to purchasing stop-loss from the payer or from a stop-loss carrier.[9] This reinsurance will protect the provider from the financial impact of catastrophic cases.

Below is a quick reference check list for negotiation considerations:

---

9   Yenson, Bruce, Kathryn Fitch, and Lynn Dong. "Evaluating Bundled Payment Contracting." Accessed September 21, 2016. http://us.milliman.com/insight/healthreform/Evaluating-bundled-payment-contracting/

Figure 10.3 Bundled Payment Negotiation Considerations

Administrative

Determine if payment will be made to one entity or by virtual bundle.

Establish when will payment be issued.

Understand if payment is made to single entity, when each provider be paid.

Identify what triggers the bundle: ICD-10 code, DRG, CPT code.

Determine duration of the bundle (clear start and end dates).

Define services to be included in the bundle; professional services, preadmission lab work, inpatient facility, implant cost, skilled nursing and inpatient rehabilitation facility, home health care, outpatient rehabilitation services, outpatient pharmacy, other.

Outline services included in the bundle by code: CPT, DRG, HCPC, ASA

Define reporting expectations: will payer provide reports demonstrating provider's performance related to cost efficiency, quality metrics and patient satisfaction?

Determine frequency of reporting: what reports will be provided by whom and at what intervals?

Judiciously select and identify care partners, define the roles and responsibilities of each.

Quality

Identify quality metrics and determine measurement methodology for each measure.

Conduct baseline assessment for each measure.

Reach agreement with care partners and payer on reasonable threshold targets for each measure.

Determine methodology to evaluate and measure patient satisfaction.

Reach agreement with care partners and payer on reasonable threshold target related to patient satisfaction.

Identify if any patient will be excluded from the bundle due to comorbidities; if yes, define comorbidities.

Financial

Ensure a clear understanding of the assumptions utilized to build the bundle payment.

Analyze historical data related to services to be provided within the bundle; past reimbursement.

Access price comparison data as available for the bundle being considered.

Determine baseline of current costs to deliver services within the bundle.

Determine budgeted amount for the episode of care (the bundle).

Determine if and when the bundle may be broken; patient excluded from bundle.

Identify how outliers will be determined and addressed.

Determine quality metrics and patient satisfaction thresholds, as applicable.

Define gainsharing opportunities and repayment parameters.

If single payment to one entity, determine payment appropriation to multiple care partners.

If virtual payment, establish true up process, including frequency, time periods and appeal process.

Consider stop-loss coverage.

In conclusion, bundled payment arrangements have the potential to reduce costs, improve quality and patient satisfaction, while simultaneously creating market and financial advantages for providers. This payment methodology has several emerging themes that are critical for success: true collaboration and coordination among care partners related to each aspect of care the patient receives within the episode, selecting care partners who demonstrate innovative approaches and are willing to challenge the status quo, physician champions who demonstrate leadership as well as health care executives that provide a high level of support.[10]

The signs all point to more bundles in the future as CMS and state Medicaid programs continue to roll out these initiatives and commercial payers begin to follow their lead. Finally, bundled payment initiatives as defined as APMs in MACRA may be applicable as Advanced APMs in the future if providers take on more than nominal risk in a bundle. The care collaboration and coordination activities required to be successful in a bundle (e.g., focus on quality and lowering costs) will assist practices in future Medicare programs regardless of the MIPS or APM paths.

---

10 Gosfield, Alice, JD. "What's Fair In Bundled Payment Contracting?" Managed Care Magazine Online. October 2013. Accessed September 21, 2016. http://www.managedcaremag.com/archives/2013/10/whats-fair-bundled-payment-contracting

Chapter 11

Shared Savings/Risk

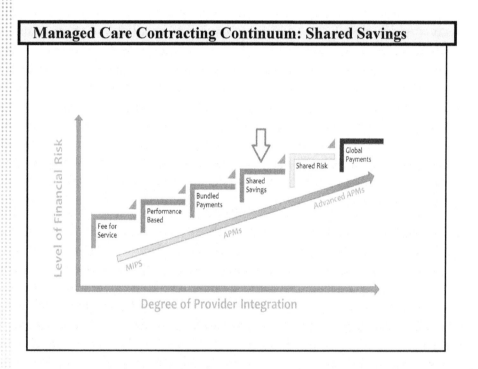

Next on the managed care contracting continuum, following bundled payments, is shared savings/risk. This risk-based reimbursement methodology offers financial incentives for provider entities to reduce healthcare costs for a defined patient population. Although not consistently presented within the context of shared savings/risk, many of the previously discussed APMs offer this methodology as a component;

some PCMH value-based arrangements, P4P contracts, and bundled payments often extend the potential for providers to share in achieved savings. For example, bundled payments encompass similar contract attributes as shared savings/risk models. Both are value-based models, but while bundled payments target a specific episode of care, shared savings/risk arrangements encompass a much larger scope of healthcare services required by a defined patient population. Again, the resounding reoccurring theme for APMs is that by coordinating care, providers and payers can deliver quality health care at a cost lower than current budgeted amounts. If, at the end of the contract term, savings exists, the payer and provider share in the savings.

Similar to other APMs, quality measures are an integral component of shared savings/risk models. In addition to having to beat the budget or cost target (total medical expense) for the defined population, it also incorporates performance-related quality measures. The majority of shared savings/risk models prohibit providers from tapping into the shared savings without meeting the mutually agreed upon quality measure targets. In addition to beating the financial budget or target, attention must be dedicated to improving the health outcomes of the defined population. Since the scope of healthcare services included in typical shared savings/risk models is expansive, the majority of these value-based arrangements are held by ACOs, CINs, and/or IPAs.

Although downside risk exists, currently the majority of shared savings/risk arrangements are limited to upside risk (about 95 percent of MSSP in 2016).[1] In upside risk arrangements, providers do not share in losses, instead they are rewarded a share of the net savings, generally in the form of a percentage of savings for their successful efforts. For example, if the actual total cost of care for patients assigned to the entity is lower than the projected budgeted costs (which may incorporate a targeted spend that is less than historical experience), the entity is eligible for a defined percentage of the difference between the actual costs and the budgeted costs (shared savings/risk). However, if the actual total costs of care exceeded the budget costs, the entity would not be responsible for the difference.[2]

Generally, the potential to secure a higher percentage of savings increases as the percentage of risk increases. Upside shared savings/risk arrangements are frequently considered to be transitional models with the end goal to incorporate

1 Murphy, John. "Accountable Care Organizations (ACOs) - Libman Education Inc." Libman Education Inc. July 15, 2016. Accessed September 21, 2016. https://www.libmaneducation.com/accountable-care-organizations-aco/

2 "Alternative Payment Models." Alternative Payment Models. Accessed September 21, 2016. https://www.aap.org/en-us/professional-resources/practice-transformation/getting-paid/Pages/Payment-Models.aspx?nfstatus=401

downside risk in the future. By limiting the risk to upside, the provider and entity have the opportunity to evolve. It takes time and resources to build the necessary infrastructure and hone the necessary skills and processes to implement changes that will result in decreased costs and improved quality. For most organizations, substantial changes are required to promote evidence-based medicine and patient engagement, monitor and evaluate quality and cost measures, meet patient-centeredness criteria and coordinate care across the care continuum. The concept of "walk before you run" is applicable.

Fueled by Section 3022 of the ACA, the MSSP has generated the greatest interest among providers. Over the past few years, providers formed ACOs, allowing them to share savings and risk with the Medicare program. An ACO is a group of healthcare providers, physicians, hospitals, and other health care professionals who voluntarily join together to provide high-quality, coordinated care to a defined population of patients. The ACO typically has a stable and strong primary care physician base. The goal of coordinated care is to ensure patients receive the right care at the right time and in the right setting while avoiding unnecessary duplication of services and preventing medical errors.[3] As frequently seen, commercial carriers quickly dovetailed onto the MSSP concept by developing and implementing shared savings/risk contractual arrangements of their own. Today, shared savings/risk arrangements exist in both private and public sectors.

Key Attributes

Reimbursement in shared savings/risk contracts is based on the fee-for-service methodology, but may include risk as well as components to reward quality and cost efficiency. Due to MACRA, participation in MSSPs is appealing for practices, as membership in Advanced APMs (which currently include MSSPs tracks 2 & 3 and Next Generation ACOs)[4] exempts providers from the potential administrative burden of MIPS reporting requirements. Shared savings/risk arrangements demonstrate the following key attributes:

- Retrospective fee-for-service payments with the potential for upside/downside risk

- Group of providers, possibly hospital and other medical professionals voluntarily join together (e.g., ACO, IPA, CIN)

- Required minimal patient threshold, defined population, and attributed lives

---

3 "Overview." Accountable Care Organizations (ACO). Accessed September 21, 2016. https://www.cms. gov/Medicare/Medicare-Fee-for-Service-Payment/ACO/index.html
4 "Notice of Proposed Rule Making: Medica Acces and CHIP Reauthorization Act of 2015." Accessed October 6, 2016. https://www.cms.gov/Medicare/Quality-Initiatives-Patient-Assessment-Instruments/ Value-Based-Programs/MACRA-MIPS-and-APMs/NPRM-QPP-Fact-Sheet.pdf

- Financial incentives to redesign, improve, and lower total cost of care

- Based on quality measures and cost benchmarks over a specific period of time

- Robust organizational infrastructure and sustainable resources needed to achieve goals

- May include care-coordination fees **per member per month** (PMPM)

- High data analytics capabilities

- High degree of clinical integration

Similar to the previously presented APMs, when participating in a shared savings/risk arrangement, providers are paid fee-for-service: provide a service, submit a claim and receive payment. The difference in shared savings/risk arrangements is that there is a mutually agreed upon budget or total cost of care target, often presented in the form of a PMPM amount. Simply, in order to receive the agreed upon percentage of shared savings/risk when all fee-for-service payments are totaled up for the defined population, total fee-for-service payments cannot exceed the mutually agreed budget or total cost of care.

Favorable and less-than-favorable outcomes are possible; therefore, successful shared savings/risk programs require a minimal number of lives to be included. At minimum, the MSSP requires 5,000 beneficiaries.[5] Commercial payers vary the minimal patient threshold generally from 1,000 to 10,000 lives. It is essential to know how many lives will be included in a shared savings/risk program.

From a timeline perspective, commercial shared savings/risk contracts are typically annual arrangements. The entity (e.g., ACO, CIN or IPA) receives baseline reports outlining cost and quality performance for the attributed lives. The entity and payer mutually agree upon targets for cost efficiency and quality. The targets are measured intermittently throughout the year (e.g., quarterly basis) and are reconciled annually. Shared savings/risk programs require a high degree of data analytics, which may come from the payer or from within the entity. Data is employed as a compass for creating action plans to improve performance.

For example, if data demonstrates high avoidable ER visits, a comprehensive action plan might be developed and implemented to promote patients contacting providers (e.g., provider education, patient education and workflow redesign) before seeking care in an ER. To succeed in shared savings/risk programs, practices must utilize the data available to proactively address opportunities for im-

---

5 "Frequently Asked Questions." Accessed September 21, 2016. https://www.cms.gov/Medicare/Medicare-fee-for-Service-Payment/sharedsavingsprogram/faq.html

provement. The payer is investing in the entity and if progress is not being made, they may choose to not renew the arrangement.

The incentives are clear: improve care and lower costs, and the provider and/ or entity will be financially rewarded. Seems like a pretty straightforward concept. But in truth, shared savings/risk models require caution. Realizing the financial benefits from these arrangements is difficult. There is a good reason why the majority of successful shared savings/risk arrangements are held by large health systems or large multispecialty provider groups. The infrastructure in terms of staff and technology required to redesign care is robust and costly. This model requires a high degree of clinical integration between care partners along the care continuum. In light of the required high startup and ongoing costs, the CMS Innovation Center created the ACO Investment Model, an initiative designed for organizations participating as an ACO in the MSSP. The model will test the use of prepaid shared savings/risk to encourage new ACOs in rural and under-served areas and to encourage existing ACOs to accept a greater percentage of downside financial risk in the future. It's not uncommon for commercial carriers to pay a PMPM to support infrastructure needs and care coordination expense. Without investment (e.g., financial, resource) from payer partners at the start of a shared savings/risk program, the likelihood of success diminishes.

Fundamental Drivers

Shared savings/risk contracts' are fundamentally centered on increasing quality while lowering costs and sharing financial rewards with participating providers. The agreements incorporate various mechanisms to hold practices accountable for performance. The fundamental drivers for shared savings/risk arrangements are similar to other APMs in that they:

- Encourage collaboration on improving efficiency and quality,

- Establish accountability between multiple providers—professional, ancillary and facility, and

- Provide access to greater financial incentives and reward providers for improving quality and lowering cost for a defined population.

In terms of encouraging collaboration with the goal of improving quality and efficiency, providers need to understand what the data indicates. Practices that are able to collaborate and successfully manage the healthcare needs of their attributed population will have access to greater financial incentives. For example, in a shared savings/risk contract, if a practice is referring to an out-of-network lab, the financial consequences to the shared savings/risk pool are significant. Another example is a surgery practice providing services in an outpatient facility setting when they could provide the service in a more cost-efficient free-standing ambulatory surgery suite. Practices must collaborate with the entire group to achieve savings and this may mean changing referral patterns and/or care settings.

Data and data analytics drives the work of the entity. For example, a CIN experienced a spike in inpatient admissions. Intuitively, they suspected cardiac cases were responsible for the increased admits per 1,000. Prior to the quarterly face-to-face meeting with the payer, the CIN requested data related to the admissions. The data did not back up their intuition; the spike in admits per 1,000 was directly related to an increase in spine surgeries. In response the CIN developed a low back pain protocol whereby primary care physicians, working collaboratively with outpatient rehabilitation providers, designed a treatment protocol for early intervention utilizing physical therapy for patients with low back pain. The goal would be to decrease total medical expense for patients experiencing low back pain (i.e., fewer MRI/surgeries and prescriptions). This can also have a positive impact on patient satisfaction, as the care redesign incorporates the physical therapist seeing patients within 24-48 hours upon referral. Accountability between providers is essential in order to achieve shared savings/risk The primary care provider and physical therapists are held accountable for following the established protocol.

If providers are successful in a shared savings/risk contract, they have greater access to financial incentives for improving quality and lowering cost for a defined population. A few examples of financial rewards include:

- Sharing savings – all participating providers in the entity can benefit if utilization/costs are well managed.

- Improved results in other programs (CMS initiatives like the VM program or Quality Payment Program[6]) – 100 percent of CMS quality program is tied to cost/quality with the same big picture goals, and performing well in one program will have a halo effect in others.

- Potential to work with payer/employer partners on evolving methodologies – payers/employers identify high performers as partners and vice versa through investing in laying a successful foundation together, and other opportunities not yet considered may be available in the future.

---

6 Quality Payment Program. Accessed September 21, 2016. https://www.cms.gov/Medicare/Quality-Initiatives-Patient-Assessment-Instruments/Value-Based-Programs/MACRA-MIPS-and-APMs/Quality-Payment-Program-MACRA-NPRM-slides-short-version. pdf

Over time, shared savings/risk opportunities will diminish as program goals are achieved. If you reach the point of diminishing returns, will there be continuing opportunities for financial rewards? There are at least two possible solutions to consider. The first is that you may be able to negotiate continued increases to sustain performance and invest in emerging technologies to care for patients. The second, increasing downside risk can be correlated with increasing upside potential even if there are fewer dollars in the pool to share assuming greater risk provides opportunity for financial gains.[7]

Negotiation Considerations

Shared savings/risk arrangements require caution. The organizational courage and cost required to successfully manage and reap financial benefits from a shared savings/risk arrangement are considerable. A well-negotiated shared savings/risk agreement creates the framework for providers to succeed. Administering these arrangements requires a highly engaged team of individuals who share common goals and are committed to deploying the principles of shared savings/risk.[8] These contractual arrangements require a multitude of negotiation considerations, including the following:

- Define the population; attributed patients

- Define services included/excluded in shared savings/risk

- Determine baseline for current cost of care

- Identify quality metrics and how they will be measured and secure baseline reports for metrics

- Determine how high-cost outliers will be addressed in terms of thresholds

- Understand if the payer has risk adjusted the population

- Determine potential upside/downside risk

Define the population: a clear understanding of the population included in the shared savings/risk program is crucial. The premise of determining savings is predicated on comparing actual costs with the anticipated unmanaged costs of a defined population; it is critical to know exactly who is included in the pa-

---

7 Bosko, Tawnya. "Understanding the Risks and Benefits of Medicare ACO Models." Accessed September 21, 2016. http://blog.thecamdengroup.com/blog/understanding-the-risks-and-benefits-of-medicare-aco-models

8 Bobbitt, Julian, Jr., and Dana Simpson. "A Checklist for Entering Shared Savings Contracts: Practical Considerations JD Supra. January 15, 2015. Accessed September 21, 2016. http://www.jdsupra.com/legalnews/a-checklist-for-entering-shared-savings-94381/

tient pool to determine baseline historical spending.[9] Thoroughly understanding where you are starting from is required. It is also necessary to understand how patients are assigned to physicians, commonly referred to as the **attribution methodology**. The attribution methodology should be clearly reflected in the contract. HMO products frequently require patients to select a primary care physician; this is usually not the case with PPO products. For the purposes of shared savings/risk models, patients enrolled in PPO products must be attributed to a primary care physician. Commercial carriers often deploy an attribution methodology based on historical claim data sometimes referred to as **plurality**, meaning the provider selected was the one that provided the most care for the patient in the past. It is important to understand how long a patient must be enrolled in the plan before their performance measurements will be included. In an MSSP, shared savings/risk arrangement assignment is determined by beneficiaries' use of primary care services provided by a healthcare professional affiliated by the ACO, most often retrospectively.[10]

Determine the scope of services that will be considered as part of the shared savings/risk agreement as well as the services that will be excluded or carved out from the agreement. Generally, shared savings/risk agreements include the full scope of healthcare services. Commercial carriers may carve out specific services such as: behavioral health, pharmacy, out of area and organ transplants services. Ensure service carve outs are clearly stated in the agreement.

Determine the baseline for the current cost of care budget. It is important to keep in mind the defined population and historical costs that will be included in the shared savings/risk program. Most frequently, the total cost of care is presented as a PMPM calculation; however, it may be presented as a percent of premium. Ensure the contracting entity has a strong understanding of how the historical cost of care has been calculated.

It is also necessary to have a strong understanding of how the payer will calculate shared savings/risk. A few examples of questions to ask include: Does the agreement include upside and downside risk? What will the distribution of shared savings/risk be, 50 percent to the provider and 50 percent to the plan? Does the provider need to hit agreed-upon quality metrics in order to participate in distribution of shared savings/risk? If possible, have the proposed

9 "Evaluating and Negotiating Payment Options." Accessed September 21, 2016. http://www.ama-assn or http://www.ama-assn.org/ama/pub/advocacy/state-advocacy-arc/state-advocacy-campaigns/private-payer-reform/state-based-payment-reform/evaluating-payment-options.page/ama/pub/advocacy/state-advocacy-arc/state-advocacy-campaigns/private-payer-reform/state-based-payment-reform/evaluating-payment-options.page

10   "CMS Releases Final Medicare Shared Savings Program Rule". Accessed September 21, 2016. http://www.klgates.com/cms-releases-final-medicare-shared-savings-program-rule-06-11-2015

methodology reviewed and tested by an outside independent source. Participating in a shared savings/risk program, even if it is limited to upside financial risk, requires a commitment from the ACO, CIN and/or IPA and from their physician member practices. There will be associated costs, such as time, dedicated staff resources to coordination care and implement practice redesign.[11]

Clearly define and understand the quality metrics to be included and how they will be measured. Secure baseline quality scores for each measure and monitor performance. Determine the role any quality scores play in shared savings/risk calculations. Some shared savings/risk agreements include provisions where savings will only be shared if quality measure targets are met. Therefore, it is of key importance to monitor quality measure performance throughout the contract term. An example of this is the BCBS Massachusetts Alternative Quality Contract, where surpluses and/or deficits are correlated directly with quality measure performance as indicated in the chart below:[12]

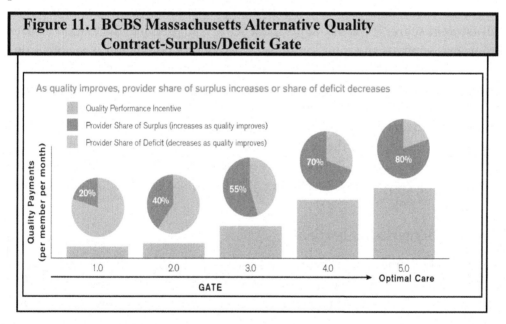

Figure 11.1 BCBS Massachusetts Alternative Quality Contract-Surplus/Deficit Gate

As quality improves, provider share of surplus increases or share of deficit decreases

- Quality Performance Incentive
- Provider Share of Surplus (increases as quality improves)
- Provider Share of Deficit (decreases as quality improves)

Quality Payments (per member per month)

20% | 40% | 55% | 70% | 80%

1.0 | 2.0 | 3.0 | 4.0 | 5.0 — Optimal Care

GATE

Determine how high-cost outliers will be handled. Commercial carriers will often set a dollar threshold, (e.g., $100,000). Once the claim expense exceeds the dollar threshold, the provider is no longer financially responsible for any future

---

11   "Shared Savings." Accessed October 06, 2016. http://www.ama-assn.org/ama/pub/advocacy/state-advocacy-arc/state-advocacy-campaigns/private-payer-reform/state-based-payment-reform/evaluating-payment-options/shared-savings.page

12   "Massachusetts Payment Refofm Model:Results and Lessons." Accessed September 21, 2016. http://www.bluecrossma.com/visitor/pdf/aqc-results-white-paper.pdf

expenditures for that particular patient. In this example, the initial $100,000 is attributed to the provider, but expense beyond the threshold is not included in the shared savings/risk calculation. The risk for the overage is assumed by the payer. If you have downside risk, consider purchasing stop-loss insurance. Stop-loss insurance establishes a maximum threshold amount beyond which a provider group is no longer financially responsible for the healthcare services for a particular patient. The coverage protects the contracting entity from unlimited losses due to catastrophic cases.

It is important to consider risk adjustment in order to understand the burden of illness for the population associated with the shared savings/risk program. Understand if and how the payer deploys risk adjustment for the defined population. Today, most commercial payers have the capability to risk adjust for a given population. We have all heard, and often rightfully so, "my patients are sicker." Risk adjustment takes into account the past services provided and the diagnosis of the patients within the defined population. The end result is a **risk adjustment score**; if the risk adjustment score is higher than the market or peer group that supports the intuition that the provider's population is sicker. Conversely, if the risk adjustment score is less than the market and/or the peer group, then the provider's population is healthier than the market or the peer group. For example, in CMS' VM program, providers whose patients have a Hierarchical Condition Category (HCC) of 75 percent or higher can receive an additional one percent incentive, if the practice is in a **bonus position**, compensating for a higher level of burden of illness.[13] These scores can impact budget targets for shared savings/risk contracts and can also be utilized in development of care management programs.

Financial Scenario Implications

Understanding financial scenarios that are included in a shared savings/risk agreement is essential. The first step is to assess your performance by understanding your baseline. This information can be obtained from the payer and compared to internal data (as available). In a shared savings/risk arrangement, data is reviewed frequently to identify opportunities for improvement, which are gleaned from the trend data analyzed. The following chart depicts an example of a comparison of baseline to current performance:

---

13   Pope, Gregory. "Evaluation of the CMS-HCC Risk Adjustment Model." March 2011. Accessed October 6, 2016. https://www.cms.gov/Medicare/HealthPlans/MedicareAdvtgSpecRateStats/downloads/evaluation_risk_adj_model_2011.pdf

Figure 11.2 Shared Savings and Risk Example Contract Math #1

Administrative Entity-Group, IPA, ACP, CIN

Care Coordination Fee	PMPM	Patients	Total Paid per Month	*Annual	*(in addition to FFS payments)
Totals	$1.50	10,000	$15,000	$180,000	

BASELINE

Category	Attributed Patients	Entity Total Paid	Entity Expected Total Paid	Variance	PPPM	Market PPPM	Variance	Performance Index
Facility Inpatient	480	$6,187,283	$7,278,243	$(1,090,960)	$55.12	$64.84	$(9.72)	0.85
Facility Outpatient	7,609	$10,419,205	$10,855,545	$(436,340)	$92.82	$96.70	$(3.88)	0.96
Other Medical Services	5,604	$3,676,842	$4,108,162	$(431,320)	$32.75	$36.60	$(3.85)	0.90
Professional	10,395	$12,067,142	$11,963,564	$103,578	$107.50	$106.57	$0.93	1.01
Totals	24,088	$32,350,472	$34,205,514	$(1,855,042)	$288.19	$304.71	$(16.52)	0.95

CURRENT

Category	Attributed Patients	Entity Total Paid	Entity Expected Total Paid	Variance	PPPM	Market PPPM	Variance	Performance Index
Facility Inpatient	416	$6,331,038	$6,417,954	$(86,916)	$64.69	$65.58	$(0.89)	0.99
Facility Outpatient	6,769	$9,582,580	$9,854,888	$(272,308)	$97.92	$100.70	$(2.78)	0.97
Other Medical Services	5,144	$3,465,878	$3,766,987	$(301,103)	$35.42	$38.49	$(3.07)	0.92
Professional	9,436	$11,621,651	$10,835,351	$786,300	$118.75	$110.72	$8.03	1.07
Totals	21,765	$31,001,147	$30,875,174	$125,973	$316.78	$315.49	$1.29	1.00

The example above reflects a sample of the high-level financial performance piece of a shared savings/risk contract. The entity receives $1.50 PMPM for care coordination fee for their 10,000 attributed lives for a total of $180,000 annually. Providers are reimbursed fee-for-service for claims submitted and adjudicated by the payer during the contract performance period.

The baseline reflects the performance established at the onset of the contract. In this example, at the time the baseline numbers were established, the entity was outperforming the market PMPM of $288.19 PMPM compared to $304.71 PMPM resulting in a variance of (-$16.52) PMPM better than the market. However, performance changed over time, as depicted in the current section, the group total cost of care went from $288.19 PMPM to $316.78 PMPM, increasing +$1.29 PMPM. The main service category with a significant variance was in Professional Services ($8.03) PMPM.

Based on previous quarterly meetings between the payer and the entity, both parties validated that the results were not consistent with the entity's care management activities. After further data analytics, it was determined the entity had four catastrophic cases all exceeding the total medical expense threshold of $100,000. Based on this performance, the entity was in jeopardy of losing their shared savings/risk contract. Due to the established collaborative relationship between the entity and the payer, the payer assisted the entity, exploring the root cause for the variance in performance. The payer explored the numerous innovative approaches the entity employed to improve quality and manage costs. It was determined that the entity's variance was created by catastrophic cases and not driven by lack of contract management and the contract was renewed.

Figure 11.3 Shared Savings and Risk Example Contract Math #2					
Professional (subset)	Non Designated Provider - Cost Per Episode	Designated Provider - Cost Per Episode	Savings Op Per Episode	Volume	Total Savings Opportunity
Orthopedics	$4,167	$4,000	$(167.00)	373	$62,291
Gastroenterology	$2,169	$2,071	$(98.00)	276	$27,048
Neurology	$4,302	$3,250	$(1,052.00)	93	$97,836
Est Potential Savings Opportunity					$187,175

Chart 11.3 (previous) depicts a subset of the total reporting package reflecting cost of care by specialty. In this scenario, the payer utilized a premium designation program for specific specialties: the top one-third of providers for cost efficiency and high quality are awarded premium designation. In this case, if a patient was referred to a non-premium-designated provider, the average cost of care was $4,167 as compared to a premium-designated provider referral, where the cost of care was $4,000—a savings of $167 per patient. This $167 bump may not appear significant; however, when volume is accounted for, the overall impact is evident— $62,291 in missed opportunity in this instance.

Figure 11.4 Shared Savings/Risk Sample Fee-for-Service Aggregate Equivalency-Baseline

Fee-for-Service Aggregate Equivalency-Baseline					104%
Actual Fee-for-Service Claims Paid to Entity					$ 16,000,000
Quality Metrics Met at the group level?					Yes
Total Member Months					120,000
	PMPM Baseline	**PMPM Current**	**Variance**	**Impact**	**Savings *50%**
Facility Inpatient	$ 65.42	$ 63.45	$ 1.97	$ 236,400	$ 118,200
Facility Outpatient	$ 100.90	$ 100.06	$ 0.84	$ 100,800	$ 50,400
Other Services	$ 54.78	$ 53.54	$ 1.24	$ 148,800	$ 74,400
Professional	$ 125.09	$ 112.87	$ 12.22	$ 1,466,400	$ 733,200
Total	$ 346.19	$ 329.92	$ 16.27	$ 1,952,400	$ 976,200
Fee-for-Service Aggregate Equivalency					106%

This table reflects the calculation for a fee-for-service equivalency under a shared savings/risk methodology. In this example, the entity was able to access the shared savings/risk amount of $976,200, resulting in a fee-for-service equivalency of 106 percent. This is favorable considering that if the entity was not participating in a shared savings/risk agreement they would have received 104 percent of Medicare in aggregate. In this example, practices participating in the shared savings/risk contract may receive an additional bonus of approximately $15,000 and the entity is responsible for fund distribution. Please note that the entity was only able to access the shared savings/risk dollars because they met their quality measures.

Regarding Medicare ACO models, all of the key attributes, fundamental drives and negotiation considerations apply, but the stakes are higher with potential downside risk for some MSSP models. The chart below[14] depicts the various MSSP and Next Generation (NG) ACO models available through Medicare:

Figure 11.5 Risk Sharing in MSSP and NG ACO Models

	MSSP			NG ACO	
	1	2	3[1]	1	2
Tracks	Upside risk only; shared savings of 50%[2] above MLR/MSR[4] of 2-3.9% with a 10% savings cap	Upside and downside risk; 60% sharing rate above the MLR/MSR of 2%[3] with a 15% savings/5-10% loss cap	Upside and downside risk; 75% sharing rate above the MLR/MSR of 2% with a 20% savings/15% loss cap	80% sharing rate for performance years 1 to 3 and 85% for performance years 4 and 5, and with a 15% savings/loss cap in all years	100% risk for Part A and Part B expenditures in each year with a 15% savings/loss cap

[1]: Track 3 is currently a proposed rule only
[2]: In the proposed rule, ACOs would have an opportunity to remain in Track 1 beyond the initial period with decreased shared savings to 40%
[3]: In the proposed rule, Track 2 would transition to a sliding scale MLR/MSR
[4]: MLR is the Minimum Loss Rate: and MSR is the Minimum Savings Rate as used by CMS

When determining whether or not to participate in one of the Medicare ACO models; or for those that are already participating and assessing their future direction, organizations need to determine how rapidly their market is changing, the implications of the model characteristics, the size of the fee-for-service Medicare market vs. Medicare advantage, their experience with managing risk, the degree to which they are already taking steps to redesign their care models, the strength of their provider network across the continuum, the size of their patient base, and the difference in financial incentives across models as well as the degree of risk aversion or acceptance for the organization. There are benefits and pitfalls to each of the Medicare ACO models, and the proposed changes to the Medicare Shared

---

14   Ibid 7

Savings Program ("MSSP") together with the NG ACO structure show that CMS is taking provider experience and comments into consideration as revisions to existing and frameworks of new models are being developed.[15]

As the incentives for participation in APMs continues to point providers toward assuming more than nominal risk, providers will need to evaluate the pros and cons associated with participation in these types of models for both Medicare and commercial populations.

Prior to entering into a shared savings/risk model, consider the following tasks outlined below in the checklist.

Shared Savings/Risk Negotiation Check List

Figure 11.6 Shared Savings and Risk Negotiation Check List			
	Yes	No	Game Plan
Administrative			
1) Is there a detailed understanding of what services are included and excluded in the shared savings/risk arrangement?			
2) Are there procedures that should be carved out and have they been clearly identified in the contract?			
3) Is there a minimal number of required lives?			
4) Is the panel size large enough?			
5) How are lives attributed			
6) Is there a strong understanding of the attribution methodology; is it stated in the agreement?			
7) Who is the defined population? Medicare? Medicaid? Commercial?			
8) What products are included? Medicare Advantage (MA), MSSP, HMO, PPO, Open-Access			
9) How can the contract be exited and what are the parameters around providing care relative to the termination clause?			

continued

---

15   Ibid 7

Check List (cont.)	Yes	No	Game Plan
Financial			
10) What are the historical costs for the population?			
11) What percentage of the services have the defined population historically received from the providers within the group?			
12) Has an outside source verified and validated the historical cost for the population?			
13) Has mutual agreement been reached regarding the budget or cost target for shared savings/risk to occur?			
14) How will attribution and retroactive eligibility be handled?			
15) Are there clear percentages for upside/downside risk for the provider and the payer?			
16) If downside risk exists, how are losses handled, including timing of repayment?			
17) If surpluses exist, when will they be paid?			
18) Does the plan provide for reinsurance to protect against catastrophic cases? If yes, at what dollar threshold?			
19) Is there a care coordination fee? If yes, how much is it? How and when is it paid?			
20) If there is a care coordination fee paid, is the fee deducted from the shared savings/risk pool			
Quality Measure			
21) What are the quality measures associated with the contract?			
22) How will the baseline for each quality measure be determined?			
23) How will each quality metric be measured? Timing?			
24) Are the targets for each quality measure achievable?			
25) Is there a minimum quality threshold that must be met prior to tapping into any shared savings/risk?			

continued

Check List (cont.)	Yes	No	Game Plan
Leadership			
26) Is there adequate physician engagement in your organization? Does the organization have a physician champion?			
27) What are the education needs within your organization to successfully administer this contract?			
28) Are there care navigators or care managers in place?			
29) What reporting will be available and supplied by the payer?			
30) When and how frequently will the reporting package(s) be available?			
31) Is there a plan for distributing surpluses and deficits across the organization through a physician bonus or compensation plan?			
32) Will administrative leadership teams and staff participate in any reward programs?			
33) How will performance be communicated to your internal stakeholders?			
34) Are there services that will be reimbursed on a fee-for-service basis? Has a method been implemented to evaluate if payments are being received and if they are accurate?			
35) How will new coverage mandates be handled within the contract?			
36) How will new technologies be addressed within the contract if they become standard of care within the term?			
37) If risk exists for pharmacy, biologicals, immunizations, and/or injectables, how will this be tracked and what happens if costs increase or if new products emerge during the term of the contact?			
38) Does the practice have the necessary infrastructure (e.g., technology, staff, analytics) to support the contract?			

In conclusion, organizational courage, robust infrastructure, and a cohesive leadership team are required to achieve a successful shared savings/risk arrangement. Success is dependent upon the ability of the organization to manage and coordinate care for a defined population across the entire healthcare continuum while maintaining focus on minimizing expense, continually improving quality and clinical health outcomes. Physician leadership, commitment and clear vision are crucial; half-hearted attempts will most likely result in failure, bringing with it the possibility of incurring significant financial loses. Conversely, as the intensifying demand from government, commercial payers, employers and the public demonstrates value, providers must continue to evaluate their readiness to transition from volume-based payment methodologies to value-based arrangements (aka APMs). Participating in shared savings/risk arrangements provides the opportunity to migrate towards value-based care while potentially reaping financial benefits for your efforts in care transformation.

Chapter 12

Capitation — Global Payment

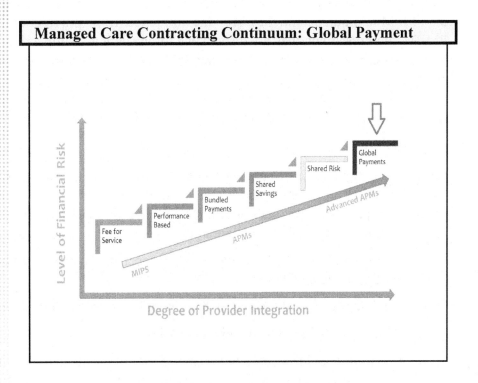

Managed Care Contracting Continuum: Global Payment

The thought of **capitation**, or **global paymen**t, strikes fear in many providers—and for really good reasons. In contrast to fee-for-service, capitation is on the opposite end of the reimbursement spectrum. This reimbursement model completely reverses the actions providers must take to be financially successful. The word capitation is derived from the phrase, "per capita," meaning per person. Capitation is essentially accepting prospective payment on a **per member per month** (PMPM) basis to cover specific services for a defined population. These arrangements involve shared financial risk among all participants, placing providers at risk not only for their performance but for the performance of other providers within the network. This payment methodology places providers at risk not only for the occurrence of medical conditions, but also for the management of these conditions. This reimbursement methodology requires a substantially different approach to both care and financial management.

In a capitated environment, the reimbursement amount is fixed regardless of the amount of services a patient may require. If the provider does not use all of the PMPM reimbursement, they keep the difference. If the provider exceeds the PMPM reimbursement, they are responsible for the deficit—simple right? "Capitation is derived from insurance principles. Actuaries construct the premium price based on historical behaviors of the providers in terms of utilization of resources. They project that utilization forward with some assumptions regarding the incidences of disease within the projected population."[1]

Key Attributes

Caring for a population of patients and assuming financial risk in a capitated contract requires providers to consider many of the same attributes as the shared savings/risk programs, but adds additional contract management administrative responsibilities. Key attributes in capitation contractual arrangements include:

- Reimbursement PMPM – typically prospective payment with potential for upside/downside risk

- Minimum patient threshold, defined population; attributed patients

- Ability to severity adjust a given population

- Group of providers, possibly hospitals and other medical professionals voluntarily joining together (e.g., multispecialty group, ACO, IPA, CIN)

- Offers financial incentives for improving care and lowering total cost of care for a given population

---

1 Gosfield, Alice, JD. "What's Fair In Bundled Payment Contracting?" Managed Care Magazine Online. October 2013. Accessed September 21, 2016. http://www.managedcaremag.com/archives/2013/10/whats-fair-bundled-payment-contracting

- Requires robust infrastructure and high data analytics capabilities (e.g., claims processing, medical management, etc.)

- Requires sustainable resources to achieve goals

- Requires high degree of integration

Capitation/global payment can be administered in multiple ways depending upon the entity's management services capabilities. In some instances, providers and/or entity may be paid prospectively on a PMPM basis or retrospectively on a fee-for-service basis with a trueing up. The total expense portion of the budget remains the same in either scenario. There are multiple scenarios to consider in capitated arrangements depending on the provider and risk category. The three main risk categories are:

- Professional risk (physician services),

- Institutional risk (facility side), and

- Payer-retained risk (administrative).

Professional and institutional risk is commonly referred to as **full risk** or **global capitation**, wherein entities take on varying responsibilities within the categories of services documented in the agreement. It is most common for capitation arrangements to be administered through large groups, multispecialty, ACOs, CINs or IPAs. It is the entity that takes the risk and determines how to administer the contract.

The minimum thresholds of lives in a capitation contract are necessary to spread the risk over a wider population. As the number of enrollees increases, the risk associated with capitation decreases, which is why large groups and/or networks typically hold these types of contractual arrangements. Additionally, these larger organizations have the necessary administrative and clinical infrastructure to manage care for the defined population. Capitation is a far riskier proposition for smaller group practices.

> The Law of Large Numbers states that the more times a random experiment is repeated, the closer the average of that experiment will be to the expected value. The law is a building block for much of statistical analysis, the idea that the mean of a large number of samples can represent the mean of the population. One example is a casino: while the casino might lose money on a single bet, over a large number of bets it will make money because the expected value of the game's probability is in the casino's favor.[2]

---

2 "Law Of Large Numbers Lesson." Chegg. Accessed September 21, 2016. http://www.chegg.com/homework-help/definitions/law-of-large-numbers-31

Regardless of the practice size, it is important to establish an actuarially sound minimum number of enrollees in order to limit risk.[3] There is no "magic number" of minimum enrollees and it is possible for small groups to do well and for large groups to have less than optimum performance depending on multiple factors.

Unlike in the late 1980s and early 1990s, today's technology allows for severity adjustment for a given population. Historically, severity adjustment did not exist; factors to determine capitation amounts were limited to the geographical region the member resided in, as well as age and sex. Technology today aggregates historical claim data, taking into account diagnoses, procedures and claim expense. This provides a much clearer picture of the severity of disease within the population.

Driven primarily by the potential for upside and downside financial risk, capitation agreements require the highest degree of integration. In full-risk capitation, the physician group, IPA, ACO or CIN accepts the risk of all primary care, specialty, institutional, ancillary services and, durable medical equipment for a defined population. Success will only be possible if physicians and hospitals work collaboratively to manage utilization and improve outcomes. In this arrangement, the entity is fiscally responsible for all services. If the entity does not perform certain services, it will be responsible for purchasing said services. Full-risk arrangements are analogous to a "mini insurance company" and may include, but are not limited to, eligibility reconciliation, financial management, utilization review, information systems management, benefit determination, medical management, provider contracting, referral management, claims processing, reporting and more.[4] Some states prohibit entities from participating in full-risk capitation while others require the entity to obtain an insurance license.[5]

In contrast to full-risk or global capitation, where the entity accepts financial responsibility for both institutional and professional services (Medicare Part A and Part B), professional capitation is accepting risk for all professional (Part B) services. Employing a high-level example at the individual provider level, a primary care physician may receive a capitated payment of $15 PMPM for providing care for 300 attributed lives. Under this arrangement, the physician receives $15 × 300 × 12 = $54,000 in total capitation payments over the course of the year. This $54,000 must cover all of the primary care services provided for the 300 attributed lives. If over the course of a year the cost of care is $50,000,

3 Model Managed Care Contract-Minnesota Edition. Accessed September 22, 2016. https://www.pdffiller. com/37287431--Model-Managed-Care-Contract-Minnesota-Medical-Association-

4 Ibid

5 Miller, Harold. "Pathways for Physician Success Under Healthcare Payment and Delivery Reforms." 2010. Accessed September 22, 2016. https://www.aace.com/files/payment-pathways-summary.pdf

the provider retains $4,000 in additional revenue (upside). If the cost of care is $60,000, then the provider absorbs the $6,000 deficit (downside). This methodology operates the same way for specialists and ancillary providers.

Although not limited to full-risk contracts, the use of **risk pool** is frequently seen within capitation contracts. Risk pools align incentives by rewarding providers who manage costs. Typically, in full-risk arrangements 10-20 percent of each reimbursement dollar is allocated to one or more designated risk pools: primary care, specialty and institutional. Throughout the year, expenses are charged against the risk pool and, at the conclusion of the year, the risk pool funds are reconciled (compared to the forecasted budget). Surpluses are distributed via a prearranged formula and deficits are generally funded from network reserves.

Risk pools are most often funded through **withholds**, meaning that part of the capitation payment is set aside to fund the pool. Utilizing the primary care capitation example, if the withhold is 10 percent, then this amount is withheld from the $15 PMPM capitation payment amount. The provider would receive $13.50 PMPM and $2.50 PMPM would be allocated to the risk pool. If targets and budgets are met, the $2.50 or a portion of it will be returned to the provider, otherwise these dollars are utilized for offsetting deficits.

The majority of capitation arrangements include **carve outs** that reflect services that are reimbursed, usually on a fee-for-service basis outside of the PMPM payment. Typically, carve out procedures are high-cost services and/or procedures such as transplant, infertility, burn care services or services such as behavioral health, which are carved out to a third-party vendor. Frequently, services that the provider group has no control over such as out-of-area emergency services are considered carve out services. Similar to shared savings, ambiguity is going to hinder success—carve out services should be clearly delineated and reflected within the capitation agreement.

In terms of process and workflow, the list of attributed members may be provided each month and often includes retrospective adjustments. Retrospective adjustments work the same way in capitated arrangements as in a fee-for-service environment—if the premium is not received within a specified time period, the entity should not accept financial liability for claims incurred on behalf of the patient, as the payer will retroactively retract the applicable number of **member months**. Member months is defined as the number of months multiplied by the number of individuals participating in an insurance plan each month. Providers assume the responsibility to seek payment for services directly from the patient. Total reimbursement equals the PMPM amount multiplied by the member months.

In order to be successful in capitated contracts, providers must have a high degree of integration. In full-risk capitation, the entity typically creates its own network and aligns incentives within the provider panel to keep patients within the network, or they risk paying for services twice. For example, if there are 25 primary care providers in the network and one sub-capitated cardiology group, the best-case scenario would be for all 25 primary care providers to refer patients to the capitated cardiologist. If a patient is referred outside of the network, fee-for-service dollars will be used to pay for cardiology services in addition to the PMPM paid to the sub-capitated cardiologist, resulting in the entity paying twice for those services. Additionally, the out-of-network cardiologist may utilize a facility that has a higher cost than selected facility partners, which may impact performance in a **risk pool**. A high degree of collaboration and integration is necessary in order to optimize performance in capitated programs—more so than any other model.

Entities can tie allocation of bonus dollars and/or capitation amounts to program requirement adherence. This is commonly referred to as **funds distribution**, and is utilized to align incentives within the risk sharing entity. For example, if in a capitated contract a network had risk for pharmacy expense and providers varied widely in terms of prescribing patterns, meaning that some providers prescribed Tier 1 medications and others did not, the entity would be being negatively financially impacted by these prescribing patterns. Incentives were identified and bonus dollars were distributed to providers who were most successful at prescribing Tier 1 medications. Communication is key and ensuring providers understand program goals/incentives; understanding the why behind the impact of prescribing patterns is critically important in risk arrangements. Successful performance in a capitation agreement is maximized with a greater the degree of provider goal alignment, transparency and integration.

Capitation reimbursement methodology provides financial incentives for improving care and lowering costs for a given population. In these types of arrangements, the primary path to success is through cost control and effective care management. Frequently cited as an inherent problem with this form of reimbursement methodology is the potential incentive to withhold necessary/appropriate care. In order to mitigate this risk, today's capitation methodologies incorporate quality metrics (similar to shared savings/risk). The goal of all value-based programs is the Triple Aim and, to that end, investing in preventative care and chronic disease management are essential in improving outcomes, lowering overall costs and increasing patient satisfaction. To effectively manage a population, volume of visits may increase, as deploying care management protocols may require patients to increase visits. For example, primary care practices should mine patient data to identify diabetic patients that have not had a hemoglobin A1c test and schedule the patient for a visit and lab test. Proactively managing patients and providing low-cost interventions (office visits/lab tests) is the goal. Think "right care, at the right time and in the right setting."

A robust infrastructure and high data-analytics capabilities are necessary to successfully manage a capitation contract. For example, entities holding the capitation contract may accept financial responsibility for claim adjudication, administering sub-capitation arrangements, monitoring leakage, establishing reserves, reconciling payer data with internal data, monitoring reinsurance thresholds and providing care management. In full-risk capitation, the entity at risk requires the need for insurance company type skills. For example, if the entity has claim administration responsibility, then it will be necessary to accrue for claims that are **incurred but not reported** (IBNR).

IBNR amounts represent dollars that are reserved to pay for future claims—determining the reserve amounts requires analysis of claims history, seasonality factors, age/sex of patients and more. Data from various sources is combined from financial systems, practice management systems (for utilization) and electronic health records, and may require outside assistance from actuaries/analysts to complete applicable analyses. For many practices involved in capitation contracts in the 1990s, not accurately reserving IBNR was a common reason for failure in these programs.

Capitation contracts require a sophisticated understanding of cost, quality and outcomes data. This data is more readily available today as some states have all payer claim databases. There are other external sources of data available (e.g., MSSP, QRUR, Area Health Resource file, the U.S. census etc.) that may be used in conjunction with entity claim data for analyses. Entities with capitated contracts may utilize an **electronic data warehouse** (EDW) to consolidate this information. Analyzing and validating the data with the payer will be an important ongoing workflow. One consideration includes tracking payments by the payer for claims that may not be the entity's responsibility. It is important to ensure that the entity is refunded for claims outside of their risk (i.e., out of area claims) and these may only be identified through back-end analyses. Establishing data exchanges with the payer on a routine basis will assist in actively analyzing and reconciling information.

Infrastructure must support sophisticated analysis and viewing the data in a variety of slices will give the network and practices insight into opportunities for improvement. Data may be analyzed in terms of provider, care setting, specialty, and diagnosis, and these data points may be reviewed together to understand if there are relational considerations that require additional attention. For example, network practices can use patient registries to assist in targeting patients that have comorbid conditions and flag these patients for enhanced care coordination. It is critical for the entity to utilize analysts to assist in these kinds of exercises and in many cases outside support may be necessary. The talent and expertise necessary to properly analyze and respond to this type of data will grow in importance as these models continue to evolve and increase in complexity.

Sustainable resources are required for success in this payment methodology. For many entities, this may come in the form of outsourced assistance, partnerships and/or internal acquisition/development of necessary skill sets. In contrast to other value-based reimbursement methodologies, capitation contracts require a higher degree of management and oversight. Establishing a sustainable foundation is necessary in order to succeed. Payer relationships are critical and meeting at least on a quarterly basis with the payer (face-to-face) to discuss contract performance and review reports is key.

There are always data issues to be managed/addressed and having committed resources and standing meetings is important in administering a capitated arrangement. These models are most successful when there is a high level of trust and integrated leadership between the providers and administrators. Working together in this type of dyad model has been a long standing indicator for better performing practices.[6] While focusing on the primary objective of providing the right care in the right setting at the right time, seek ways to work collaboratively.

Fundamental Drivers

The fundamental drivers in a capitation contract are similar to those in shared savings/risk arrangements. At the core, entities/practices that are able to collaborate and successfully manage the healthcare needs of their attributed population will have access to greater financial incentives for improving cost, quality and outcomes. In this Advanced APM (i.e., NG ACO) —the degree of difficulty is high and it requires significant investment in terms of infrastructure and organizational courage. In order for success to be achieved, commitment to managing care in a capitated environment requires involvement from the entire organiza-

---

6 Zismer DK, Brueggemann J. Examining the "dyad" as a management model in integrated health systems.Physician Exec. 2010 Jan-Feb;36(1):14-9

tion. This challenge is heightened when providers included in the arrangement are disparate. Fundamental drivers for this APM include:

- Encourages collaboration on improving efficiency and quality
- Focuses on population health management – **risk stratification**
- Establishes accountability between multiple providers
- Provides access to greater financial incentives; rewards providers for improving quality and lowering costs for a given population

Capitation requires a high degree of collaboration in order to improve efficiency and quality of care. There are many examples of collaboration that are essential here, both internal to participating practices and external. Internally, it is everyone's job to "get their head in the game," from the team member scheduling the patient to the medical assistant rooming the patient to the billing/collection team. For example, a patient contacts a primary care practice to schedule a sick visit. The scheduler needs to be considering "how do we get them in here today?" to minimize the possibility of an urgent care or ER visit. This workflow generates a conversation with the clinical/care management team to determine the best course of action. Perhaps fitting the patient in by shuffling the schedule or scheduling a visit late in the day would be the best course of action. Understanding the central goals by all involved triggers the optimum sequence of events that contribute to providing the best care in the most cost effective setting while increasing patient satisfaction.

In terms of external collaboration, take for example that the group has subcontracted with an Ear, Nose and Throat (ENT) practice for specialty care. This same patient seen on the same day for the sick visit requires referral to the ENT. During check-out, the appointment could be secured. The check-out staff member needs to be mindful of selecting the appropriate panel provider (e.g., capitated specialist) or else the entity will pay twice for the care. In terms of the billing and collections team, if the ENT group selected was from the non-capitated group, the entity must pay the provider fee-for-service and alert the leadership team regarding the expense which will in turn impact reserves. The decisions made all the way through the patient experience matter and are impactful.

Search the Google search engine for "population health management" and a plethora of definitions and vendors claiming to have found the successful population health management Holy Grail can be found. Simply put, population health management is about caring for patients holistically and proactively. It is thinking about their healthcare needs even when they themselves may not be. It is about connecting the dots early to more actively manage patients and maintain health. For example, if the entity has 5,000 members to manage, they will include males and females representing a variety of age groups with unique healthcare needs. One of the first necessary steps in managing this population is identifying potential needs and categorizing them based on how much care may be required—think of it as high/medium/low (**risk stratification**). In addition to identifying where they lie in terms of these general categories, trend movement between the groups. There are various ways to categorize patients and approaches include, but are not limited to, the following:

- Hierarchical Condition Category

- Adjusted Clinical Groups®

- Elder Risk Assessment

Hierarchical Condition Category (HCC) is a component of a payment attribution methodology developed by CMS to adjust Medicare Advantage health plan payments at the patient level based on burden of illness.

> This means that two patients within the same community can have a different payment rate based on factors relating primarily to the amount of risk—or work—it takes to maintain the health of a patient. Risk adjustment allows CMS to pay plans for the risk of the beneficiaries enrolled, instead of an average amount for Medicare beneficiaries, according to CMS guidance on the subject. By risk adjusting plan payments, CMS is better able to make appropriate and accurate payments for enrollees with differences in expected costs. Risk scores measure individual beneficiaries' relative risk and are used to adjust payments for each beneficiary's expected expenditures. Several factors impact the risk score, but primarily the HCC risk adjustment is based on the enrollee health status and their demographic characteristics. The combination of the health status [combined with] demographics characteristics determine the patient's Raw Risk Score.

> **Raw Risk Score = Patient Demographic Score + Health Status**

> Since the physician cannot influence the age and sex of the patient, the real impact that a physician can have on the Raw Risk Score (and therefore on payment) is the accurate documentation of the patient's Health Status by billing the proper diagnoses codes.[7]

---

7 "The Medicare Advantage HCC Program: Why and How to Optimize Your Coding." April 29, 2014. Accessed September 22, 2016. https://www.healthfusion.com/blog/2014/health-topics/medical-coding/medicare-advantage-hcc-program-optimize-coding/

Basically, the higher the HCC, the sicker the patient. Patients with comorbid conditions would have a higher than average HCC score. Care for individuals with multiple comorbid conditions can cost up to seven times more that care for others with only one chronic condition.[8] HCCs are captured through diagnostic coding (ICD-10 codes) and it is important to rigorously maintain complete and accurate clinical documentation and coding routines, as they have tremendous impact in capitation contracts.

HCCs are one way to risk stratify, but there are others. The Johns Hopkins Adjusted Clinical Groups® (ACG®) system was developed at The Johns Hopkins Universityand focuses on the diagnostic and/or pharmaceutical code information found in insurance claims or other electronic medical records. ACGs provide a comprehensive representation of the morbidity burden of populations, subgroups or individual patients—as a **constellation of morbidities**, not as individual diseases and was not developed with Medicare population at the core.[9] The Elder Risk Assessment (ERA) was designed for patients over the age of 60 and utilizes claim data to identify risk of hospitalization and emergency room visits. Gathering this information from payer partners will serve as the foundation for identifying a population's potential patient care needs.

Once patients have been risk stratified, it is possible to establish systems (care management and technology based) to provide a comprehensive clinical picture of each patient in the population. Identifying best practices using evidence-based guidelines will enable the entity to determine next steps in managing the population. Participating practices will utilize clinical/care management staff and business intelligence programs to combine data with EHR and practice management information to track and target patients for care management opportunities. For example, a pediatric practice tracking Gardasil® immunizations may contact patients who have not completed the series. Helping the population manage their health by addressing needs proactively can hopefully prevent future health problems through focusing on long-term health goals.

Capitation contracts require accountability between multiple providers in a variety of care settings. Success in this methodology requires a high degree of collaboration and physician engagement. The practice and all of its team members, associates and outside partners are all in it together, and the successes and/or failures of all involved are interdependent. A common area of focus in many APMs is cost management in the post-acute care setting, where understanding the

8 "The High Concentration of U. S. Health Care Expenditures." June 2006. Accessed September 22, 2016. http://archive.ahrq.gov/research/findings/factsheets/costs/expriach/expendria.pdf

9 Johns Hopkins ACG System. . Accessed September 22, 2016. http://acg.jhsph.org/index.php/the-acg-system-advantage

quality and cost of care can assist in identifying which post-acute setting and/or facilities are the best fit (i.e., partnering with the high quality/low cost providers) supporting APM goals. Transparency is key—successful entities track, trend and share referral patterns, adherence to best practices in terms of evidence-based guidelines and workflows, spend per specialty, prescribing patterns, etc.—by provider—which can indicate if the team is rowing together. Transparency also provides opportunity to course correct, which is very important in these types of programs. Identifying assumed versus actual actions provides accountability at the provider level and is essential for success.

In capitated contracts, there is access to greater incentives and rewards—success breeds success in these programs. The potential financial rewards can come from various sources:

- Improved cash position with prospective payments – PMPM payments are received each month regardless of resource consumption

- Sharing in risk pool attributions – all can benefit if utilization/costs are well managed

- Improved results in other programs (CMS initiatives such as VM) – 100 percent of this program is tied to cost/quality and performing well in one program will have a halo effect in others

- Potential qualification as an Advanced APM, which starting in 2019 qualifies for a 5 percent annual lump sum bonus based on Medicare revenue, added 0.75 percent increase in Medicare payments starting in 2026 and waives MIPS reporting requirements[10]

- Ability to attract and retain high-performing providers

- Potential to work with payer partners on evolving methodologies – payers identify better performers as partners and through investing in laying a successful foundation together other opportunities may arise

These are a few examples of the potential rewards of exploring this type of payment methodology. There will be practices that are more appropriately positioned to participate in these kinds of arrangements than others. The greater the risk, the greater the potential reward—which is the case in capitation. In the 1990s, capitation contracts across the country failed, but many of today's agreements have added components (such as quality measures) that may make this methodology sustainable. Determine where the practice resides relative to

---

10 MACRA: Delivery System Reform, Medicare Payment Reform. Accessed September 20, 2016. https://www.cms.gov/Medicare/Quality-Initiatives-Patient-Assessment-Instruments/Value-Based-Programs/MACRA-MIPS-and-APMs/MACRA-MIPS-and-APMs.html

risk readiness in order to discern if and when a capitated model may make sense for the practice.

Negotiation Considerations

Capitation contracts vary from fee-for-service arrangements in that the entity is most commonly paid on a prospective PMPM basis for a population of patients rather than on a fee schedule rate for each service provided. In the capitation methodology, the budget is based on the PMPM amount. The PMPM amounts are based on predicted costs for the population associated with many variables (i.e., age, sex, health status, geography). These are generally the same attributes that are used in determining premium amounts. In entering this type of arrangement, it is critical to determine if the PMPM amounts are adequate to cover the cost of care (based on contractual responsibility) for the population. Understand what supplies, pharmaceuticals, biologicals, injectables and immunizations may be included/excluded from these agreements to ensure a clear understanding about financial responsibility. Below are general recommended steps for assessing a capitation rates:

1. Identify the services that are included/excluded,

2. Define the population of attributed patients in the panel and understand attribution methodology,

3. Understand historical total medical cost for the population, and

4. Define how entity/practice costs compare to PMPM proposed.

This first step in this process is understanding the **division of financial responsibility** (DOFR) and it is important to obtain this information in terms of a common reference point (i.e., CPT, HCPCS, ICD-10 and Hospital Revenue Codes). Below is a sample chart to provide a high-level guide using categories of service.[11] The payer will typically provide this information, but be sure to further define the level of specificity to ensure that there is clear delineation regarding what is included/excluded from the PMPM budget amount. The Integrated Healthcare Association (IHA) also has a DOFR available for reference.[12] The following chart is a sample chart to provide a high-level guide using categories of service.

Sample Division of Financial Responsibility Matrix *(Next 4 Pages)*

---

11   Payment Innovation-Integrated Healthcare Association. Accessed September 21, 2016. http://www.iha.org/our-expertise/payment-innovation

12   Ibid.

Figure 12.1 Financial Responsibility Matrix			
Service Description	**Group**	**Hospital**	**Payer**
Acupuncture – Medical – OP			
Allergy – Serum – OP			
Allergy – Testing & Treatment – OP – Professional			
Ambulance (Air and Ground) – OP			
Amniocentesis – OP – Facility & Professional			
Anesthesiology – IP & OP – Professional			
Autologous Blood Services – OP – Facility & Professional			
Biofeedback (Medically Necessary) – OP			
Chemical Dependency (Detox) – IP & OP – Facility			
Chemical Dependency (Detox) – IP & OP – Professional			
Chemical Dependency (Rehab) – IP & OP – Facility			
Chemical Dependency (Rehab) – IP & OP – Professional			
Chemotherapy (Including Chemotherapy Drugs – Inject/Oral) – OP – Facility & Professional			
Chemotherapy – IP – Professional			
Chiropractic – Medical – OP			
Chiropractic – Supplemental			
Circumcision – OP – Facility & Professional			
Complimentary & Alternative Medicine			
Diabetic Supplies (test strips, lancets, syringes, etc.)			
Diagnostic Tests – OP – Facility & Professional			
Diagnostic Tests – Specialized Scanning – OP – Facility & Professional			
DME – IP			
DME, Ostomy/Colostomy Supplies, Prosthetics/ Orthotics – OP			
Emergency Room – OP – Facility			
Emergency Room – OP – Professional			

Service Description	Group	Hospital	Payer
Endoscopic Studies – IP – ER Physician			
Endo Endoscopic Studies – OP – Facility			
Endoscopic Studies – OP – Professional			
Family Planning – OP – Facility			
Family Planning – OP – Professional			
Fetal Monitoring – OP – Professional			
Health Education – OP			
Health Evaluation/Physical			
Hearing Aids/Molds – OP			
Hearing Screening (Audiologic Evaluation) – OP			
Hemodialysis / Dialysis – IP & OP – Professional			
Hemodialysis / Dialysis – OP – Facility (including all drugs)			
Home Health Care			
Hospice Services – IP – Facility & Professional			
Hospital Based Phys Interpretative Services, including Radiology & Pathology – IP & OP – Professional			
Hospitalization Services – IP – Facility			
Immunizations & Inoculations (Medically Necessary) – OP			
Infusion Therapy – OP – Facility			
Infusion Therapy – OP – Professional			
Injectables – Not Part of Outpatient Pharmacy Benefits – OP			
Injectables – High Cost Injectable Program – Drugs			
Injectables – High Cost Injectable Program – Administration			
Injectables –Self Administered and Office Based – Drugs			
Injectables –Self Administered and Office Based – Administration			

Service Description (cont.)	Group	Hospital	Payer
Laboratory/Pathology (Diagnostic Only) – OP – Facility			
Laboratory/Pathology (Diagnostic Only) – OP – Professional			
Laboratory/Pathology – IP – Facility			
Lithotripsy – OP – Facility			
Lithotripsy – OP – Professional			
Massage Therapy – Medical – OP			
Medication – Prescription – OP			
Medical/Surgical Supplies (casts, splints, bandages) – Office – OP			
Mental Health – Crisis Intervention – OP – Professional			
Mental Health – IP & OP – Professional			
Mental Health – IP & OP – Facility			
Naturopathic Physician Services – Medical – OP – Professional			
Observation Room – OP – Facility			
Oral Surgery / Dental Services – Accident & Injury Only – OP – Facility			
Oral Surgery / Dental Services – Accident & Injury Only – OP – Professional			
Out of Area – IP & OP – Facility			
Out of Area – IP & OP – Professional			
Outpatient Surgery – OP – Facility			
Outpatient Surgery – OP – Professional			
Physician Services (All Professional Services) – IP & OP – Professional			
Prosthetics – Surgical Implants			
Radiation Therapy – IP & OP – Professional			
Radiation Therapy – OP – Facility			
Radiology (Diagnostic Only) – OP – Facility			
Radiology (Diagnostic Only) – OP – Professional			

Service Description (cont.)	Group	Hospital	Payer
Radiology – IP – Facility			
Reconstructive Surgery – IP & OP – Professional			
Reconstructive Surgery – OP – Facility			
Rehabilitation – Cardiac/OT/PT/RT/ST – OP – Facility			
Rehabilitation – Cardiac/OT/PT/RT/ST – OP – Professional			
Skilled Nursing Facility – IP – Facility			
Sleep Studies – OP			
TMJ – Evaluation (excludes dental exams/treatment) – OP – Professional			
Transfusions – OP – Facility			
Transplants (excluding corneal and skin) – Candidacy & Maintenance – IP & OP – Facility			
Transplants (excluding corneal and skin) – Candidacy & Maintenance – IP & OP – Professional			
Transplants (excluding corneal and skin) – Transportation			
Transplants (excluding corneal and skin) – IP & OP – Facility			
Transplants (excluding corneal and skin) – IP & OP – Professional			
Urgent Care – OP – Facility & Professional			
Vision – Medical Treatment – OP – Professional			
Vision – Refraction for Contact Lenses/Frames – OP – Professional			
Vision Care Materials – Contact Lenses/Frames (non-cataract) – OP			

In terms of how capitation amounts are arrived at by the payer, premium distribution sets the stage for understanding the DOFR and the big picture. Simply stated: payers collect premium dollars from employers which are utilized to pay for healthcare services. Payers cover administrative costs and medical claim expense costs with premium dollars. The chart below depicts a high-level example of how these costs might be allocated by premium dollar:[13]

Figure 12.2 Premium Dollar Distribution Example	
Total Premium	100%
Payer Retained (administrative expense)	16% - 18%
Primary Care providers	10% - 13%
Specialist providers	27% - 30%
Facilities	30% - 33%
Outside Providers	2% - 3%
Pharmacy Expense	9% - 11%

In a capitated arrangement, based on the chart above, the payer will propose PMPM rates considering information depicted above along with other factors (i.e., geography, historical utilization, demographic information). Once the framework is established in terms of the DOFR, the next step is to define members attributed and associated attribution methodology. Members may be assigned by PCP or attributed based on other methodologies such as **plurality of care** (meaning the provider with the most claim expense receives attribution). The payer should provide a list of enrollees who will be assigned to the entity and update this on a monthly basis. As discussed earlier, securing a large enough population is a very important consideration from a risk perspective. Utilize the following types of information to analyze reasonableness of the proposed capitation amounts:

- Age/sex of each patient – this will help identify demand for services (i.e., high number of children may indicate the need for more pediatric coverage).

- Risk adjustment for each patient – obtain this information from the payer for items such as the following: diagnoses, co-morbid conditions, social economic status, physical function status, psychosocial functioning, race, substance abuse.

---

13   Capitation Source book – page 90   http://www.ache.org/pubs/hap_companion/gapenski_finance/
online%20chapter%2020.pdf

- Utilization profile – obtain by CPT code by patient and use to monitor expected utilization to budget.

- Demographic considerations – understanding where the population resides, which can assist in determining service needs (i.e., if high number come from lower income neighborhoods, there could be transportation issues).

- Employers (current and future) – utilize to understand (based on industry) what types of health issues may impact utilization and what the payers' plans are in terms of marketing.

- Product variances – understand how, if moving from open access to a gatekeeper design, this may impact utilization (e.g., if primary care patients need a PCP visit before obtaining care from specialists).[14] There are many details to evaluate, and entities/providers considering entering into these types of arrangements should contemplate obtaining actuarial guidance in analyzing data and comparing historical expense trends to PMPM proposals. Additionally, request the payer to provide certification from their actuary that the projections are actuarially sound. If this is not provided, request an explanation regarding how the PMPM proposal amounts were established. The following chart (next page) is an example cost table based on demographics:

---

14 Model Managed Care Contract-Minnesota Edition. Accessed September 22, 2016. https://www.pdf-filler.com/37287431--Model-Managed-Care-Contract-Minnesota-Medical-Association-

Figure 12.3 Estimated Demographic-Based Rates

| | | | Cost per member per Month | | | | | |
| | | | Primary Care | | Specialist Care | | Facility | |
Age Band	Male	Female	Male	Female	Male	Female	Male	Female
0-1	1.9	2.1	$47.00	$47.00	$32.00	$32.00	$28.00	$28.00
2-4	2.8	2.9	$18.00	$18.00	$12.00	$12.00	$17.00	$17.00
5-19	12.4	12.4	$11.00	$11.00	$12.00	$12.00	$16.00	$16.00
20-29	13.6	11.4	$11.00	$11.00	$18.00	$50.00	$12.00	$55.00
30-39	19.6	10.3	$13.00	$18.00	$24.00	$45.00	$25.00	$61.00
40-49	5.3	5.9	$15.00	$20.00	$33.00	$42.00	$51.00	$52.00
50-59	43.6	4	$21.00	$23.00	$46.00	$47.00	$80.00	$67.00
60 - 69	0.6	0.4	$24.00	$25.00	$75.00	$61.00	$121.00	$86.00
70+	0.3	0.5	$26.40	$27.50	$82.50	$67.10	$133.10	$94.60
Total	50.1	49.9						
	100							

Compare the historical utilization (total medical expense) to the potential panel to be served and request higher-level data (shown above) from the payer. Apply historical utilization information to derive a fee-for-service equivalency (see **financial scenario implications** on page124) and compare to proposed PMPM amounts. This will become the baseline and can be used in negotiations with the payer. Using their data as a basis for the analysis is critical. Examine what-if scenarios to evaluate rates such as:

- What is the potential decrease in administrative expense for the plan with fewer claims to process? Delegated credentialing and utilization review?

- What is the increase in administrative expense to the entity for administering the program and how is this compensated?

- What opportunities are there for decreasing utilization (i.e., if sub-capitating to a narrower panel of specialist) and what could be the economic impact?

- What is the potential economic impact of increased utilization as preventive care drives more patient visits and how does that figure into the equation?

- How are the long-term gains connected in terms of measurement to short-term goals?

- How are new technologies and new drugs accounted for?

- What mechanisms are available to revise the capitation amount during the course of the contract?

These are but a few suggestions. Based on the type of capitated arrangement, this should be expanded to account for other factors. The establishment of the baseline PMPM distribution is a critical step as all of the "dominoes" align from this starting point.

Administrative responsibilities in capitated arrangements are an important consideration. These may include accepting capitated payments and submitting encounter data to the payer and comparing capitation dollars to estimated fee-for-service rates. Or it could be as complex as establishing a mini insurance carrier where the entity delegates a broad spectrum of responsibilities (e.g., credentialing, eligibility reconciliation, claims processing, utilization review, etc.). Understand administrative responsibilities associated with the contract and identify the cost associated with these functions. Payers on average retain up to 15 percent - 18 percent of premium dollars for administrative responsibility and components of these may be passed along based on entity responsibilities.

Some responsibilities may be **delegated**, meaning the payer verifies that the entity has the necessary infrastructure, technology, policies & procedures and staffing model to support the administrative function(s). These could include the following: credentialing, provider relations, claims processing, case management, actuarial costs, utilization review, funds distribution and more. Investment in additional infrastructure is commonly necessary (i.e., case management applications, accounting services) to support administration of the contract. Identify the additional administration costs and ensure they are captured. Obtain the economic support necessary to successfully administer the contract.

Reinsurance or stop-loss insurance helps protect against losses associated with catastrophic cases (e.g., transplants, neonatal intensive care). Stop-loss insurance establishes a maximum threshold amount beyond which the entity will no longer be financially responsible for the costs of care. This type of insurance can be secured (at times) through the payer or the insurance market. It works much like other insurance coverage. For example, if the threshold is $10,000, once the entity has provided services worth this amount, the carrier would cover (on a fee-for-service basis) expenses for care over the $10,000 threshold. Once again, analysis expertise will be necessary to aggregate these amounts and file claims for reinsurance on an ongoing basis. This is not necessary in all capitated arrangements, as it depends upon the amount of risk assumed. [16]

Capitation contracts today commonly have associated quality metrics which must be well understood and have an established baseline as well as a communication process established. The rigor with which these measures are monitored and managed is of great importance. Many agreements incorporate minimum acceptable thresholds and the share of risk pools and/or deficits may even be on a sliding scale based on quality metrics. Entities that are successful in these arrangements connect the quality metric dots with outcomes and use this information to reinforce transformation activities.

Financial Scenario Implications

Understanding the necessary foundation for managing a capitation contract is a foundational step in evaluating the potential for this type of APM. Keep in mind that this could be a successful endeavor, as MGMA research indicates that practices with capitation contracts received 36 percent more revenue than those that rely only on fee-for-service reimbursement. Practices with higher capitation revenue also have higher staffing and technology expenses, however, due to the resources needed to run a risk-based payment system.[15] Assess proposed rates by plugging in the historical utilization data to determine the fee-for-service equivalency using the following approach:

15   Ritchie, Alison, Donna Marbury, Daniel R. Verdon, Chris Mazzolini, Salynn Boyles. "Shifting Reimbursement Models: The Risks and Rewards for Primary Care." Medical Economics. April 8, 2014. Accessed September 22, 2016. http://medicaleconomics.modernmedicine.com/medical-economics/content/tags/aca/shifting-reimbursement-models-risks-and-rewards-primary-care?page=full

Figure 12.4 Capitation Example Contract Math

Capitation	PMPM	Patients	Total Paid per Month	Annual	
Totals	$7.50	5,000	$37,500	$450,000	

CPT	Description	Contracted Rate Payer A	Medicare	%Mcare	Total Volume	Est. Total Payment= Rate* Vol	Est. Total Medicare Payment= Mcare*Vol
99213	Office Visit	$75	$70	107%	5,000	$375,000	$350,000
69210	Ear Wax Removal	$65	$50	130%	500	$32,500	$25,000
90471	Immunization Admin	$20	$25	80%	500	$10,000	$12,500
83036	Glycosylated Hemoglobin Test	$8	$15	53%	500	$4,000	$7,500
Totals						$421,500	$395,000

Fee-for-Service Aggregate Equivalency		107%
Capitation Amount	$450,000	
Quality Metrics met at the group level?	Yes	
	Est Impact	FFS Equivalency
Variance to Capitation Allocation	$28,500	121%

In addition to determining if capitation rates are appropriate in comparison to fee-for-service, evaluate what-if scenarios to examine worst-case scenarios. One scenario to model would be if the withhold on the capitation reimbursement reaches the maximum and the practice is in a deficit position at the end of the contract term, how would that impact the practice? What are the financial implications if quality measure goals are not met? Invest in ensuring that the relationship with partners (e.g., facilities, payers, specialists) is solid and that both confidence level and trust is where it needs to be to navigate the ups and downs (which are a given). This is probably the most critical part of the process because even if things do not work out ideally during the course of the contract, having a good working relationships increases the likelihood of successfully navigating the experience.

Below is a negotiation checklist, which can serve a guide, that summarizes the more salient considerations for a capitation contract:

Figure 12.5 Capitation Contract Check List			
Check List	**Yes**	**No**	**Game Plan**
1) Are the services included and excluded in the capitation payment well understood? (DOFR)			
2) Are there procedures that should be 'carved out' of the contract and have they been clearly identified in the contract? (DOFR)			
3) How does the capitation PMPM amount compare to historical costs? Are the PMPM rates actuarially sound?			
4) What additional administrative costs might the practice incur and have those been accounted for in the PMPM rate(s)?			
5) What will be the timing for monthly capitation payments?			
6) How will retrospective adjustments occur?			
7) Has a standard communication pathway been established (i.e., assigned representative, monthly standing meetings) with your payer partner?			
8) Is the panel size large enough?			
9) Is there adequate physician engagement in the organization? Is there a physician champion?			
10) What are the education needs within the organization to successfully administer this contract?			
11) Has reinsurance been secured to protect against catastrophic cases? Have the necessary reserves been established?			
12) What are the quality metrics that will be incorporated into the contract and has the payer committed to an adequate rhythm in terms of production, review and reconciliation of these analyses?			
13) Will it be necessary to contract out for services not provided by the practice? If so, does the practice have a plan for contracting?			

Check List (cont.)	Yes	No	Game Plan
14) Is there a system in place for distributing surpluses and deficits across the organization through the physician compensation plan?			
15) Will administrative leadership teams and staff participate in any reward programs? How will those be administered?			
16) How will the practice communicate performance to internal stakeholders? How often?			
17) Are there services that will be reimbursed on a fee-for-service basis? Has a method been implemented to evaluate if payments are being received and if they are accurate?			
18) How will new coverage mandates be handled within the contract?			
19) How will new technologies be addressed within the contract if they become standard of care within the term?			
20) If you have risk for pharmacy, biologicals, immunizations, injectables - how will this be tracked and what happens if costs increase or if new products emerge during the term of the contact?			
21) Does the practice have the necessary infrastructure (e.g., technology, staff, analytics) to support the contract? What are the gaps?			
22) If there is a withhold, is it reasonable? What has been the track record in terms of distribution?			
23) Can the practice identify any "low hanging fruit" like transitioning site of care to less costly settings or augmenting referral patterns and can the financial implications be estimated?			
24) How can the contract be exited and what are the parameters around providing care relative to the termination clause?			

Another consideration is **fund distribution**. If in a surplus position, how should/ could those dollars be allocated to the providers? Of course, seek the advice of an attorney to ensure compliance with current legislation. There are many ways to distribute surplus incentive dollars, but probably the most common method is a blend of distribution by performance indicators. This can include various data points such as:

- Number of assigned members,
- Patient satisfaction,
- Quality metrics,
- Readmission rates,
- Spend per beneficiary,
- Spend per capita,
- Generic prescription utilization rate,
- Hospitalization rates per 1,000,
- Provider engagement,
- Patient access and more.

The following chart is a sample score card from the CareFirst program[16] as described in their 2014 PCMH Program Performance Report:

Figure 12.6 Primary Care Score Card

PCP Engagement	35 points	Patient Access	15 points
PCP Engagement with the PCMH Program	7.5 points	Online Appointment Scheduling	3 points
PCP Engagement with Care Plans	7.5 points	Unified Communication Visits / Telemedicine	3 points
Member Satisfaction Survey	7.5 points	Office Hours Before 9:00am and After 5:00pm on Weeknights	3 points
Program Consultant Assessment	10 points	Office Hours on Weekends	3 points
Program Representative Assessment	2.5 points	Overall Patient Experience	3 points
Appropriate Use of Services	20 points	Structural Capabilities	10 points
Admissions	8 points	Use of E-Prescribing	2 points
Potentially Preventable Emergency Room Use	4 points	Use of Electronic Medical Record (EMR)	2 points
Ambulatory Services, Diagnostic Imaging and Antibiotics	8 points	Meaningful Use Attestation	2 points
Effectiveness of Care	20 points	Medical Home Certification	2 points
Chronic Care Maintenance	10 points	Effective Use of Electronic Communication	2 points
Population Health Maintenance	10 points		

16 2014 PCMH Program Performance Report. July 30, 2015. Accessed September 21, 2016. https://member.carefirst.com/carefirst-resources/pdf/pcmh-program-performance-report-2014.pdf.

Here are primary care and specialist examples from the Capitation Source Book:

Figure 12.7 PCP Bonus Allocation Example	
Measure	*Points*
Inpatient Admissions/1,000	15
Hospitalization Rate/1,000 - Acute Ambulatory Care-Sensitive Conditions	15
Readmissions	15
Coding and documentation	10
Patient satisfaction	10
Compliance with policies and procedures	15
Per Capita Cost	10
Total	100

A critical factor is having providers engaged and involved in methodology development. It is important that participating providers are on the same page and that the criteria and math are easy to understand and transparent. Establishment of these methodologies can be incorporated into current committee structures or an ad hoc group of leadership can be responsible for ownership of the initiative.

Additionally, providing interim updates regarding scoring can help keep everyone on course and give the entity opportunities to iteratively reconcile variances. This challenging model is a radical departure from traditional reimbursement methodologies—there will be a learning curve, so proactively communicating performance and diving into the heart of matters will assist in navigating a capitation agreement.

Figure 12.8 Specialist Bonus Allocation Sample Model	
Measure	*Points*
Inpatient Admissions/1,000	15
Hospitalization Rate/1,000-Acute Ambulatory Care-Sensitive Conditions	15
Readmissions	10
Coding and documentation	15
Patient satisfaction	10
Compliance with policies and procedures	15
Per Episode Cost	20
Total	100
Total	100

Chapter 13

Setting up to Succeed

"By failing to prepare, you are preparing to fail."
— *Benjamin Franklin*

There are many ways for medical practices to prepare for future success. It all starts with committing to invest in laying the necessary groundwork. There are multiple dimensions to developing and maintaining a strong managed care contracting strategy. The first piece of the foundation is establishing the practice's **Value Proposition.** Once the Value Proposition has been developed, survey the market, evaluate current contract performance and utilize this information as a compass to inform a contracting strategy. Establishing a successful contracting strategy requires ongoing oversight and a contract monitoring system. Better performing practices consistently demonstrate these common characteristics.

- Define practice roles and responsibilities for contracting activities with clarity

- Analyze contract performance thoroughly and establish baseline performance

- Establish timelines for negotiations based on historical performance

- Secure a provider champion to support the process

- Understand that a well thought out approach pays off

- Take emotion out of the equation

- Put the past behind them

- Focus on creating a collaborative relationship with payer partners – and understand that it will not be perfect for anyone

- Focus on both short- and long-term goals

- Consider new approaches/measures and assist the practice in "growing" into value-based arrangements

It is never a perfect process and it is often filled with many twists and turns. Enduring the inevitable challenges is very much part of this journey. It is important to understand that the payers are figuring it out as well, so practices that build collaborative relationships are setting themselves up for a more comfortable ride.

One of the biggest hurdles in the process can be the past. Practices and payers have not been very successful previously at crafting trusting relationships for a variety of reasons. Payer tactics vary widely and range the entire spectrum from reasonable to completely unscrupulous. It is hard to find a practice that comments positively about the contract negotiation process. But it is a new era—and practices that are able to turn over a new leaf with payers will benefit. Like most anything else in life, it is always easier to work with people you like. Keep this in mind as the practice sets out to carve a new path.

The high-level steps below can help the practice lay out a successful managed care contracting strategy.

Figure 13.1 High Level Steps for Managed Care Contracting	
Step 1	Develop a Value Proposition
Step 2	Complete a market/payer assessment
Step 3	Complete top code analysis and establish a modeling mechanism
Step 4	Engage in negotiation
Step 5	Evaluate contract language
Step 6	Monitor contract performance

Developing a Value Proposition

A Value Proposition explains how your services solve customers' problems or improves their situation. Ideally it tells the customer why they should obtain services from you and not from the competition. The Value Proposition tells the practice story. This information should be crafted into a hard copy deliverable that can be used as a reference point during payer negotiations. Value Propositions answer the following questions:

- Who are you as a practice?

- What value does the practice add to the network?

- How can the practice quantify how it adds value?

- Why is the practice better than its competition?

- Where does the practice see itself on the managed care contracting continuum?

A Value Proposition contains information about the practice framed by addressing the areas in the chart:

Figure 13.2 Value Proposition Chart		
Practice Information & Differentiators	Goals & Ratings	Common Ground
Practice Locations	Outcomes	Critical Questions

Value Propositions focus on a few strategic areas addressing key facts in a succinct and powerful way. Initially the focus is on practice general information, including provider information, services provided, volume of visits, hospital affiliations and locations. This is where the practice sets the stage for describing organizational "nuts and bolts." While this may seem unnecessary, since payers already have a good understanding of this information, it may be surprising what new information is being communicating to the payer. In addition to this information, define what makes the practice unique. It could be that the practice is part of a narrow network, Center of Excellence or that the majority of the physicians were trained at the top medical schools in the country. From a payer perspective, knowledge about the practice in large measure is limited to their payer profile data, specialty, number of providers and location. It is up to the practice to bring to light the additional details that will assist the payer partner in understanding the practice on a deeper level. This is relationship building 101.

Differentiators are the next segment of the Value Proposition. They are where the practice adds details around the attributes that make the practice stand out from the competition. There are many ways in which the practice may be able to differentiate itself, including the following:

- Access (i.e., evening hours, email communication with patients)

- Accreditations (i.e., PCMH, Center of Excellence)

- Technology (i.e., patient portal, electronic medical records, telehealth)

- Alternative payment models (i.e., BPCI, MSSP, value-based contracts)

- Value-add services (i.e., Pharm D staff, ADHD clinic)

- Community service (i.e., newsletters, sports teams, charity care)

This piece of the Value Proposition should give the audience insight about the attributes the practice possesses that are above and beyond the competition. It should demonstrate that the practice contributes to the health and wellbeing of its patient population; therefore, the economic incentives need to be aligned in order for the practice to continue to provide the level of care that is being delivered. For example, if the practice has attained PCMH Tier III status, it is well documented that these practices provide high value to their patient population. In the *2013-2014 Overview of PCMH Effectiveness*, peer reviewed studies found that PCMHs experienced:

- 60 percent cost improvements

- 93 percent utilization improvements

- 66 percent quality improvements

- 100 percent access improvements

- 100 percent satisfaction improvements

These improvements associated with PCMHs are beneficial to the practice, payers and patients.[1] This can be utilized in communications with payers to support the practice's position in negotiations. For example, if the practice's access is expanded, it could quantify the volume of patients seen and attribute a portion of them to cost savings associated with an ER visit. It has been estimated that

---

1 Nielsen, Marci. "The Patient-Centered Medical Home's Impact on Cost and Quality." January 2015. Accessed September 22, 2016. https://www.pcpcc.org/download/5499/PCPCC 2015 Evidence Report. pdf?redirect= node/202076

the average "extra" cost if a patient goes to the ER instead of an office is \$580.[2] If the practice sees 60 patients over the course of a month during weekend hours, and an estimated 25% of them may have otherwise gone to the ER, the practice potentially saved the healthcare system about \$100,000 over the course of a year. This type of quantification can be a valuable leverage in dialogues with payer partners.

Mission statement, goals and ratings are another key area of focus in development of the practice Value Proposition. The mission statement is a written declaration of the practice's core purpose. Many times, information from the practice website can be used as a starting place and then the wordsmithing begins until the practice arrives at a one- or two-sentence message that captures its fundamental purpose.

If there are goals that should be described in addition to the mission statement, those should be placed in close proximity to provide additional dimension. It is also important to determine how the practice rates in terms of quality and efficiency with the payers. Use these payer ratings to demonstrate that the practice is achieving accolades with payers, including government programs like the CMS Physician Compare, if appropriate. Be sure to outline if the practice has been included in any narrow networks and specify how the selection criteria worked, if appropriate.

From a transparency viewpoint, research how the practice stacks up to peers from a cost and quality perspective. There are a few different resources to examine in order to identify cost comparisons including payer websites and various other tools discussed in **Chapter 5: Transparency**. Prepare, do the homework in this area to understand how the practice compares to its peers. Many of these ratings are provider-specific and some sites will also assign overall practice ratings, so be sure to review all of the details.

There have been many instances where providers uncover misinformation during this process (e.g., providers no longer with a practice continue to be linked) and understand that patients are viewing this information with increasing frequency. In the case that the practice's ratings are not what one would hope for, fold addressing these issues into the practice priorities. If the data demonstrates that the practice stands out from the competition, be sure to mention this in the Value Proposition.

The outcomes section is probably one of the most challenging sections to complete, but it is also the most critical. It is all about what a practice does to create

---

2 "Reducing Inappropriate Emergency Department Requires Coordination with Primary Care." September 2013. Accessed September 22, 2016. http://www.rwjf.org/content/dam/farm/reports/issue_briefs/2013/rwjf407773

value and improve health outcomes. Below are a few examples of what practices have used in this section, including potential sources:

Value Proposition Sample Outcomes Sources

Figure 13.3 Value Proposition Outcomes and Sources	
Outcome Measures – Compared to Peer Group	Source
Readmission Rates	Hospital Partners and/or Quality and Resource Use Reports (QRURs)
Length of Stay	Hospital Partners
Vaccination Rates	Payer Partners (Commercial & Medicaid), CDC
Well Visit Rates	Payer Partners (Commercial & Medicaid)
Diagnostic Tests - interpretation time	Hospital Partners
Avoidable ER Visits	Payer Partners
Generic Prescription percentage	Payer Partners
Hospitalization Rates per 1,000 by condition	QRURs, Payers
Infection Rates	Hospital Partners
HEDIS Measures	Payer Partners and/or Quality Reporting
Patient Satisfaction	CAHPS® or Internal Information

This is an area where charts can work well. Here are a few examples:

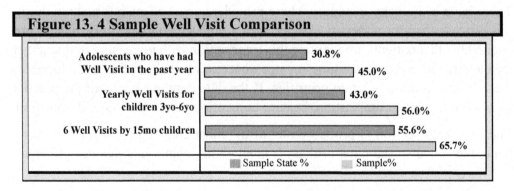

Figure 13. 4 Sample Well Visit Comparison

Adolescents who have had Well Visit in the past year	30.8% / 45.0%
Yearly Well Visits for children 3yo-6yo	43.0% / 56.0%
6 Well Visits by 15mo children	55.6% / 65.7%

■ Sample State %   ■ Sample%

Figure 13.5 Sample Diagnostic Test Time for Interpretation of Stroke

Tracks the time to interpretation for stroke patients. As "time is brain", a quick diagnosis on a potential stroke patient can improve the patient's outcome and potentially save cost of treatment over time. The door to interpretation time on stroke CT of the head is less than 20 minutes on average, which is below the goal time of 45 minutes.

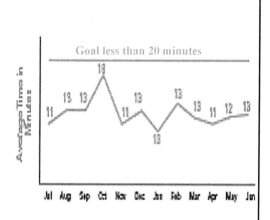

Figure 13.6 Facilty Utilization Comparison

Outcomes			
Practice	Peer Variance		
2013-Sample Payer	My Peds	Peers	Variance
Convenience Care Visits	17	52	-67.3%
Potentially Inappropriate ER Visits	41	45	-8.9%
Urgent Care Visits	128	209	-38.8%
Hospital Admissions	9	12	-25%

In presenting this information, describe the impact that these measures have on quality and cost of care. Exact numbers on how many dollars the practice saves given its focus on these areas is not required, but have an idea about what that could mean. For example, we described earlier that the extra cost for an ER visit is $580 a patient. Assess this for the practice and have it available during payer discussions. Understanding the practice's value will position it for sharing in the savings with a value-based contract. This is another area where homework is extremely important. One great source of information for practices is Medicare's QRUR, which contains data around outcomes that are quantified and scored compared to peer groups. This report is produced by CMS twice a year each spring and fall and can be downloaded from the CMS website at (https://portal. cms.gov/). Starting in 2019, this type of data will also include more episodic care cost information and the frequency of distribution may change.[3] While Medicare populations differ from commercial, as long as practice focus and approach to care is consistent across populations then the similarities can be drawn for comparative purposes.

To prepare the section on common ground, the first step is to take a look at the payer website. Invest an hour and read the press releases, provider resource section, new product offering information and be sure to take a look at what they are presenting to brokers and members. Take your impressions and compare to the practice goals and mission. Are there any similarities? Major differences? Synergies? Take this information and articulate where the practice's goals/purpose might overlap with the payer and create a table and/or image that represents this intersection. Below is an example of what some practices identify during this process as an effective way to anchor discussions in this area:

Figure 13.7 Triple Aim

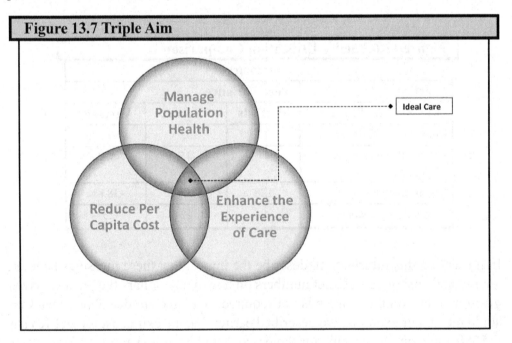

3 MACRA: Delivery System Reform, Medicare Payment Reform. Accessed September 20, 2016. https://www.cms.gov/Medicare/Quality-Initiatives-Patient-Assessment-Instruments/Value-Based-Programs/MACRA-MIPS-and-APMs/MACRA-MIPS-and-APMs.html

This exercise will help anchor conversations regarding how the practice's focus on patient care aligns with payer objectives. By framing the discussion around commonalities, the practice can hone in on how it can work with payers to help propel each other forward in attaining mutually beneficial goals.

The final component of the Value Proposition is identifying essential questions that need to be addressed during the course of negotiations with the payer. This is dependent upon the practice's goals for the conversation. If the goal is to work with the payer to develop a bundled payment arrangement, frame a question to that end. If the practice desires to add quality measures like patient access to the agreement, pose a question that asks the payer how this type of contract works with their panel. Develop these questions and include in writing in the practice's Value Proposition. Many times the Value Propositions are passed along internally at the payer. This practice information and the type of arrangements that interest the practice will provide the payer representative with what they will need to go to bat for the practice. Below are a few possible questions for the payer:

- What types of contracts are you offering our specialty in this region?

- How can we work together in new/different ways?

- Are you looking for a pilot practice to explore how new arrangements might work?

- What are some pertinent issues relative to our specialty that we should be discussing?

- What new product offerings will your organization be rolling out in this market?

- Are there any products/networks that we are not part of and if so, why not?

- Do you have any data that you can share with us relative to how we stack up to peer groups? Is this information provided to members? If so, how?

These questions will come up as the practice pulls the information together for its Value Proposition. Place the most critical questions (perhaps the top three) in the body of the document to ensure that there is discussion. Use these questions to jumpstart the dialogue around how the practice can work with the payer to move its contracts out of fee-for-service mode and into fee-for-value mode.

Market/Payer Assessment

Now that a Value Proposition has been created, it is time to take a closer look at what is happening in the local market for top payers. The best way to approach this is to first identify what payers represent a significant revenue for the practice. Usually a handful of agreements become the focal point. Identify these payers by determining how much total revenue each contract drives to the practice and delineate by product if possible. Compare the revenue for each payer to charges, as in this example below:

Figure 13.8 Sample Payer Mix and Gross Collections Chart				
Payers	**Total Charges**	**% Payer Mix**	**Total Revenue**	**Gross % Collections**
Payer 1	$ 1,000,000	17%	$ 700,000	70%
Payer 2	$ 500,000	8%	$ 300,000	60%
Payer 3	$ 750,000	13%	$ 590,000	79%
Payer 4	$ 250,000	4%	$ 100,000	40%
Medicare	$ 1,500,000	25%	$ 1,000,000	67%
Medicaid	$ 500,000	8%	$ 300,000	60%
Commer-cial	$ 750,000	13%	$ 600,000	80%
Self-Pay	$ 500,000	8%	$ 400,000	80%
Others	$ 250,000	4%	$ 200,000	80%
Total	$ 6,000,000	100%	$ 4,190,000	70%

In addition to the obvious financial considerations, assign a "hassle factor" rating for each payer in order to understand estimated administrative costs. One way to quantify is to seek feedback from billing staff and examine the following metrics: **accounts receivable** (AR) over 90 days, days in AR, ease of authorizations/pre-certifications/referrals, denial volume, ease of communication with payer. These hidden costs are impactful and are important to consider as the practice moves toward more complex arrangements. Assign this hassle factor rating on a scale of A to F and incorporate into the negotiation process.

Public information exists through the Department of Insurance Rate Filing for major payers. Although not often utilized in negotiations, this data provides information about payer performance trending for the last five years, such as:

- Premium five-year trend

- Revenue, net income and expense by category (medical/administrative)

- Product information and member counts

- Management analysis, retrospective and prospective

- **Medical Loss Ratio** (MLR) (% of premium an insurer spends on claims and expenses that improve health care quality)[4]

Practices can review this information and determine if there are any important details that may be helpful during the negotiation.

Utilize the Value Proposition and **Payer Assessment** to identify what is feasible and/or desirable for the practice from an operational, technological, cultural and administrative perspective. The managed care contracting continuum outlines the various methodologies to consider:

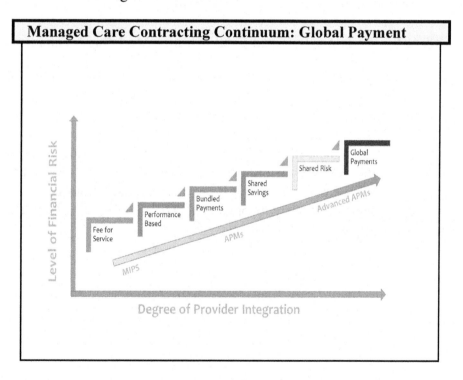

4 Medical Loss Ration. The Center for Consumer Information & Insurance Oversigh. Accessed September
   22, 2016. https://www.cms.gov/CCIIO/Programs-and-Initiatives/Health-Insurance-Market-Reforms/
   Medical-Loss-Ratio.html

Much of this is new territory for payers and providers. Understand that the payer may already have an opinion about your readiness. It is important for a practice to identify if there are gaps in terms of what the market is demanding and where the practice is in terms of value-based contract readiness. In some cases, the practice may line up nicely with what the market is offering or perhaps there is work to be done to prepare for next generation contracts. In any case, begin to chart the course and develop competencies, secure resources and most importantly start the dialogue with payer partners.

Keep in mind that even if the practice is not completely prepared to take on a new methodology, it may make sense to explore the possibilities through the negotiating process as it may assist in identifying opportunities to prepare for next generation managed care contracts. Proactively exploring value-based managed care contracting possibilities provides a practice the opportunity to potentially participate in crafting/defining these arrangements. If a practice is not taking the lead, the competition might seize the opportunity.

Complete Top Code Analysis and Establishing a Modeling Mechanism

A top code analysis is identifying the CPT codes driving 80 percent to 90 percent of practice revenue. This is accomplished by extracting data from a practice management system (or billing company) and obtaining for a one-year time period: payer, CPT code, modifiers (as applicable), total payments and volumes/units. Ensure that the date range selected is at least 90 days prior to the current time period in order capture the most accurate reflection of revenue. Depending on specialty, size, and practice composition, this can range from 10 CPT codes to over 100 for large multispecialty practices. The following chart (next page) is a simplified example of this type of analysis:

Figure 13.9 Sample CPT Code Analysis					
CPT	**Description**	**Total Volume**	**Est Total Payment = Rate*Voll**	**% of Total Revenue**	**Top Codes**
99213	Office Visit	5,000	$ 375,000	79%	85%
69210	Ear Wax Removal	500	$ 32,500	7%	
90471	Immunization Administration	500	$ 10,000	2%	
83036	Glycosylated Hemoglobin Test	500	$ 4,000	1%	
Other codes			$ 75,000	15%	
Totals			$ 496,500		

Use this information to create a modeling mechanism (many practices use Microsoft Excel as a primary tool here). A modeling mechanism should include current contract allowables, current year Medicare rates (see the CMS website: *https://www.cms.gov/Medicare/Medicare-Fee-for-Service-Payment/Physician-FeeSched/index.html*) and should capture the information depicted in the following table:

| | | | | **Figure 13.10 Top CPT Code Revenue** | | | | |
CPT	Desc	Total Volume	Contracted Rate Payor A	Est Total Payment (Rate *Vol)	Medi-care	%Mcare (Rate/ Medicare	Est Total Medicare Payment (Mcare*Vol)
99213	Office Visit	5,000	$ 75	$ 375,000	$ 70	107%	$ 350,000
69210	Ear Wax Removal	500	$ 65	$ 32,500	$ 50	130%	$ 25,000
90471	Immunization Administration	500	$ 20	$ 10,000	$ 25	80%	$ 12,500
83036	Glycosylated Hemogloin Test	500	$ 8	$ 4,000	$ 15	53%	$ 7,500
Totals				$421,500			$ 395,000

Take the total Estimated Payments in Column E and divide that by the total Estimated Medicare Payments in column H to arrive at the aggregate percentage of Medicare = 107 percent. This foundation can be used in determining the initial proposal and evaluating payer responses. To establish an initial proposal, utilize the following information:

- Current aggregate percentage of Medicare for each payer
- Gross collections for each payer
- Average reimbursement per visit/service
- Length of time from last increase
- Hassle factor
- Current term of contract
- Current rate of the Medical Consumer Price Index (MCPI), which can be found at the Bureau of Labor and Statistics website (http://www.bls.gov/cpi/)

Utilize this information with your payer/market research, outcomes data, negotiation history, and Value Proposition to determine the initial proposal. Also, utilize the transparency information to identify local market trends in terms of reimbursement and incorporate into the managed care contracting strategy. The chart below is a guide to summarizing the data in order to craft an initial proposal:

Figure 13.11 Sample High Level Initial Proposal Grid				
SAMPLE	Payer 1	Payer 2	Payer 3	Payer 4
% Payer Mix	17%	8%	13%	4%
Gross Collection Rate	70%	60%	79%	40%
Avg. Reimbursement/Visit	$ 58	$ 55	$ 62	$ 31
% Medicare	115%	105%	130%	90%
Hassle Factor	D	D	C	B
# years since last negotiation	4	8	8	never
Contract Term	2 years	3 years	evergreen	evergreen
Last Negotiation increase	2.50%	5%	15%	NA
MCPI	3.2	3.2	3.2	3.2

Engage in Negotiation

"Begin with the end in mind"

—Stephen Covey

The foundation for the negotiation has been developed. The next step is to initiate a request for negotiation, which may be accomplished by written correspondence, email, phone call or requesting a meeting. Include in the initial communications with the payer the practice's Value Proposition as appropriate. If an in-person meeting is possible, use that time to walk through the Value Proposition and include a practice provider in the meeting with the payer. The goal of the interaction (e.g., meeting, email, phone call) is to provide insight to the payer about the practice and the value it provides to the network. Use the Value Proposition to guide the discussion and invite the payer to share current plan initiatives. The practice can glean an in-depth understanding of the current business initiatives at the payer (e.g., system platform migrations, new products, etc.). It is acceptable to let the payer know that a proposal will follow, but don't let that muddy the waters, as the intent is to provide information about the practice Value Proposition, learn about payer priorities and open the door for collaboration.

After this interaction, submit the initial proposal in writing which provides the foundation for tracking (email communication is optimum). Ensure documentation of all future communications, noting any verbal mutual agreements. Manage the process with rigor from start to finish. Reach mutual agreement for defined actions and timelines, setting the stage for realistic expectations. Average timeline for negotiations is 120 to 180 days and at times longer dependent upon complexity of the negotiation.

If working toward a value-based methodology, expect the timeline to increase. Providers may experience a high degree of frustration during this part of the process, which requires super-human tenacity. If the payer is not responsive, a practice may have to work its way up the chain of command until a contact is identified who is willing to assist. Keep in mind, a big piece of this approach is an investment in what will hopefully become a new collaborative relationship.

Anticipate that the payer will respond with an offer that is less than requested and/or the value-based components lack clarity. Use the methodology described earlier in this chapter to determine the overall net financial impact to revenue by subtracting the estimated increase from the estimated current revenue. Payers do not desire to be disadvantaged by the competition and at times it can be useful to compare experience across payers and leverage this during negotiations. For example, if one payer is reimbursing more than another, present the spread in terms of percentage points, while not revealing payer-specific data. Many payers mine this data through Coordination of Benefits (COB) analysis and may be cognizant of this information.

Factor in the potential upside/downside risk associated with value-based components, as applicable. If the methodology is new for the practice, stress test the concepts with clinical teams to ensure what is proposed is within reason. Understand the operational implications and include key stakeholders in the decision-making process. Once vetted in terms of fee structure and value-based components, prepare a counterproposal and submit to the payer. Repeat this process until the parameters of the new agreement are within the realm of reasonableness. If additional clarity around a new methodology is necessary, ask the payer to meet with the practice or participate in a conference call to address questions. If possible, provide the questions ahead of time to allow time for research. It is optimal to secure a multi-year contract, including automatic escalators, to save administrative burden on both sides.

Evaluate Contract Language

Once agreement is reached on rates and value-based components, the next piece to address is contract language. Use the Fee-for-Service Negotiations Key Considerations Chart (p. **48**) in Chapter 8: Fee-for-Service as a starting point to identify potential problematic language. Document each concern in terms of current language, proposed revision and rationale as outlined in the example below:

- Current: Group may terminate this agreement within 180 days of contract effective date.

- Proposed: Group may terminate this agreement within 90 days of contract effective date.

- Rationale: 90-day term window consistent with other major payer contracts.

Providing this level of detail ensures that communication accurately reflects desired revisions. In contract language discussions, depending on federal/state law and leverage, there will be wins and losses. Generally speaking, payer policy and procedure manuals are referenced throughout the agreement, therefore they must be reviewed. These manuals are typically available on payer websites.

Multiple resources exist that can help with contract language review, some free and some for purchase. The American Medical Association (AMA) has a toolkit that may be used to search and compare model contract language. State medical societies may provide toolkits, which vary in comprehensiveness from state to state. Of course, depending on the situation, a practice may elect to consult an experienced healthcare attorney or consultant for guidance.

If the negotiation is not successful, careful consideration and extreme caution should be exercised with regard to termination. Termination may be possible provided the termination window is open. The termination window can be found in the agreement and is based on contract effective date and term of the agreement. For example, if the practice can issue termination 120 days at the end of the initial term, identify that date and validate this understanding with the payer. Termination may be a successful strategy, but should be used as a last resort. The best-case scenario is that the negotiation process has resulted in the following for a practice:
- Improved financial performance.
- Cultivated an enhanced payer relationship.
- Improved understanding of payer's strengths/weaknesses.

- Secured or positioned the practice for a value-based arrangement.

- Established game plan for the next round of negotiations.

This is an ongoing process. Anticipate that some wins will be financial, others will be positional and some will be relational. All of the benefits have merit and a successful negotiation encompasses a combination of these attributes. It is critical to help the entire practice, including staff and providers, in understanding new methodologies and the ultimate goals. It is much more than $5 a visit to be gained in next-generation contracting—it is about carving a sustainable, mutually beneficial relationship, and it can be done.

Monitor Contract Performance

Monitoring the contract performance is where the rubber meets the road. The onus is on the practice to establish and maintain a contract monitoring system. Below are the key components of a comprehensive contract monitoring system:

- Complete a contract quick reference guide (sample found in **Chapter 8: Fee-for-Service)**.

- Load allowables into your practice management system.

- Monitor payer website regularly.

- Keep your finger on the pulse of denial and/or administrative burden issues.

- Plan for the next round of negotiations in terms of timing.

The quick reference guide includes all of the pertinent information needed at a glance. It should include contact information, effective date, product listing, fee schedule type, pay for performance parameters, carve outs and other key facts. Each contract negotiation should have this document created or revised as a book end. Many practices keep this information available either in a contracting notebook or in electronic form. This information should be shared with key staff. Many times, billing and/or denials management protocols are also catalogued with this document. Using the quick reference guide in concert with other revenue cycle management tools is a means to ensure that the contract is being administered as anticipated.

Loading allowables into the practice management system ensures that negotiated rates are monitored and are consistent with contract terms. Often, contracts include language stipulating a claim may be appealed within a specified time frame (e.g., 180 days from date of payment). If it is determined payment is incorrect and the payer is not notified in the timeframe outlined in the agreement, then the payer may not be responsible for payment.

There are instances that the payment amount is not off by much—for example within $2 of the negotiated rate. If the practice has a manual spot check approach to the payment posting, staff members may overlook these variances. The payer may provide notification of fee schedule updates with a short timeframe for response. Frequently these notices are addressed to the participating provider, but to ensure adequate review, it is critical for the communications to be directed to the responsible party within the practice.

Monitoring the payer website is a common oversight practice in managing contracts. Payer provider manuals reflect policies, and procedures can be revised on a frequent basis. Monitoring payer websites is the most expeditious way to stay current regarding changes. A best practice is to assign a responsible team member to monitor these websites for updates. Below is a checklist that can be used for monitoring payer provider manual updates:

Figure 13.12 Sample Payer Informational Review Check List		
Payer 1	**Date**	**Comments**
Payer contacts: emails, address, phone #s, titles		
Monthly connection call (large practices)?		
Provider links (locations/credentials/ quality scores) validated?		
New relevant policies & procedures?		
New product announcements?		
Transparency information reviewed?		
Pertinent formulary changes?		
System updates?		
Other manual updates?		

Monitoring denials and/or process issues is an important part of contract monitoring. Billing staff typically have insight regarding denials, management issues and workflow challenges. Tracking AR indicators as discussed earlier in the chapter, along with capturing billing staff feedback, will provide a comprehensive view of contract performance.

| Figure 13.13 Sample Contract Monitoring Grid | | | | | | | | | | |
Payer	Total Annual Charges	Total Annual Payments	Collections %	% Aggregate RBRVS	% Payer Mix	Last Round Increase %	Effective Date	Termination Window	Administrative Burden Rating	Last Round Negotiation Key Comments	Next Renegotiation Start Date
Payer 1											
Payer 2											
Payer 3											
Payer 4											
Payer 5											
Payer 6											
Payer 7											
Payer 8											
Payer 9											
Payer 10											
Payer 11											
Payer 12											
Payer 13											
Payer 14											
Payer 15											
Payer 16											
Payer 17											

At the conclusion of the current negotiation, begin planning for the next negotiation cycle. Consider the length of time it took to negotiate the current agreement, contract termination window and any other pertinent factors. The chart below provides guidance for tracking key data points:

Utilize a tracking mechanism to ensure that the negotiation cycle is followed. One of the more common missteps involves practices neglecting to initiate renegotiations as outlined in the negotiation cycle. Time is money, and it is difficult to make up for lost time in contract negotiations. Working on incremental increases on a more frequent basis typically yields more favorable results. Incorporating this rigor in the contracting cycle sets practices up for a much clearer view of contract performance. Establishing and executing a comprehensive contract monitoring system ensures that negotiation benefits are realized by the practice.

Chapter 14

Conclusion

"In times of change, learners inherit the earth, while the learned find themselves beautifully equipped to deal with a world that no longer exists."
—Eric Hoffer, American philosopher and author of
The True Believer:
Thoughts on the Nature of Mass Movements

We hope that the guidance provided in this manuscript will assist your organization in navigating the shifting volume to value tides. It starts with identifying where you are and defining where you want to be through developing a clear understanding of market dynamics (national/local, commercial/government), potential arrangements available within your local market and connecting those dots with your organization's goals. In conjunction with exploring these models, much of this book was dedicated to "connecting the dots" to assist in providing not only the "nuts and 'bolts" for the methodologies but transparency around how the pieces fit together. Understanding the framework and methodology possibilities sets the stage for action. Now that the frame of reference has been established, your practice can begin to experiment with these arrangements, if so desired. Considering the healthcare affordability crisis, ACA, MACRA, CMS Innovation Models and commercial payer value-based contracting strategies will enable providers to prepare for the unprecedented amount of financial risk they will experience. Moving from fee-for-volume models represents an evolution in clinical and payment methodologies that focus on creating quality outcomes, foster greater accountability and utilize substantial innovations in medical technology, all requiring a higher degree of risk from providers relative to payment for services. In contrast, fee for value models intend to align incentives across providers, members, employers and payers to improve clinical outcomes and the patient experience, along with improving cost efficiency, potentially achieving the Institute for Healthcare Improvement's Triple Aim. Ultimately, this is what it is all about and the decisions made along the way by your practice will have far reaching impact more than any other time period we have experienced.

About the Authors

Doral Jacobsen, MBA, FACMPE is CEO of Prosper Beyond, Inc., a specialized healthcare consulting firm nestled in beautiful Asheville, North Carolina.

Doral is a seasoned healthcare consultant with over 20 years of experience serving healthcare providers ranging from solo practitioners to large academic medical centers. She is a popular speaker and author, always looking around the corner to help her clients prepare for 'what's next'.

Doral is known for assisting practices with next generation managed care contract negotiations, revenue cycle and payment reform. She is a Fellow in the American College of Medical Practice Executives. Doral graduated from Florida Atlantic University with a bachelor's in health services and obtained her master's in business administration from Webster University in Denver, Colorado.

Doral has authored numerous articles on medical practice revenue cycle, managed care contracting and payment reform is a frequent speaker at national, regional and local healthcare forums.

 NANCI L. ROBERTSON, RN, BSN is a health care consultant specializing in managed care contracting. Nanci has thirty years of experience working in the health care field. Her primary emphasis is negotiating managed care contracts on behalf of physicians, Independent Practice Associations and ancillary providers.

Prior to starting Robertson Consulting, Inc. in 2000, Nanci worked in several clinical positions as a Registered Nurse. Her managed care experience included managing and directing the Health Services, Provider Relations and Provider Contracting Department for a national carrier. Additionally, Nanci served as the Site Administrator for a physician management organization responsible for the administration an implementation of global capitation contracts for commercial and Medicare populations.

Most recently, Nanci spends her time putting together the puzzle pieces of health care reform. Her primary goal is to provide calm in the midst of chaos by assisting her clients with clear, concise, actionable work that promotes the Triple Aim and develops a long term vision and strategy in the rapidly changing health care environment.

Nanci holds a Master of Arts in Organizational Development from the University of Phoenix, and a Bachelor of Science in Nursing from Loretto Heights College.

Index

A

ACA 27, 32, 39, 99
  levels 21
  provision requirements 20
Accountable Care Organizations (ACOs) 6
accounts receivable (AR) 152
ACO
  hospital-led 13
  physician-led 13
acquisition cost
  expenses 56
Advanced Alternative Payment Model (APM) 3, 60, 63, 64
  types 63
Affordable Care Act, The (ACA) 3
Agency for Healthcare Research and Quality (AHRQ)
  quality metrics 36
algorithms
  payment/fee schedules 44
Alternative Quality Contract (AQC) 12
American College of Surgeons (ACS) 36
American Heart Association (AHA) 36
apitated contracts
  how to be successful in 120
appropriate screenings
  50-70 years 72
attribution methodology 104

B

Berwick, Donald 11
best-case scenario
  results 159
BPCI initiative 85
bundled payments 7, 81
  CMS initiatives 83
  financial considerations 92
  fundamental drivers 89

innovation models 84
key attributes 87
negotiation considerations 90, 93
standardization 88
trueing up 83
virtual bundle 83
Bundled Payments Programs 63, 67

C

capitation 115, 123. *See also* global payment
key attributes 116
per member per month (PMPM) 116
capitation contract check list 138
capitation/global drivers
fundamental drivers 123
capitation/global payments 7
carve outs 119
delegated (responsibilities) 135
financial responsibility matrix 128
financial rewards 126
financial scenario implications 134
fund distribution 139
funds distribution 120
incurred but not reported (IBNR) 121
limit risk 118
member months 119
negotiation considerations 127
plurality of care 132
risk categories 117
Risk pools 119
withholds 119
capitation source book 141
carve outs 119
capitation/global payments 119
case rates
fee for service method 44
categorizing patients
risk stratification 124
Center for Medicare and Medicaid Services (CMS) 11, 32
Centers of Excellence
transparency tools 33
CJR and Cardiac Care Demonstration (risk dependent) 4, 64
claims submission 48
Clinically Integrated Networks (CINs) 12
CMS data portal (website) 67
CMS initiatives
bundled payments 83

CMS Innovation Center initiatives 64
Collaborative Accountable Care (CAC) 12
common ground 150
Commonwealth Fund
  significance of Triple Aim 12
Comprehensive Care for Joint Replacement (CJR) Model 85
Comprehensive ESRD Care (CEC) 4
  model 64
Comprehensive Primary Care Plus (CPC+) 4, 64
constellation of morbidities 125
Consumer Assessment of Healthcare Providers and Systems (CAHPS)
  quality metrics 36
consumer-driven plans 18
contracting strategy
  common characteristics of a successful 143
contract quick reference guide 57
coronary artery bypass graft (CABG) 82
cost-efficiency. *See also* quality performance measures
  measures 66
cost visit analysis 55
CPT 4 codes 47
CPT code analysis 154
CPT code review 155
CPT codes 45, 55, 154

D

decreasing waste 31
delegated (responsibilities)
  capitation/global payments 135
denial volume 152
Department of Health and Human Services 3
Department of Insurance Rate Filing 152
discounted fee-for-service 43
Discount off billed charges
  fee-for-service method 44
division of financial responsibility (DOFR) 127
documented monitoring process 67
durable medical equipment (DME) 32

E

ease of authorizations/pre-certifications/referrals 152
ease of communication with payer 152
Elder Risk Assessment (ERA) 125
electronic data warehouse (EDW) 121
electronic health record (EHR) 62, 125
episode-based payment initiatives

bundled payments 84
establish accountability 70
Evaluation and Management (E&M) codes 57
evaulate contract language 158
Explanation of Benefits (EOB) 48
external collaboration 123

F

fee-for-service 5, 7, 43
  methods 44
  reimbursement 48
  typical arrangement 54
fee-for-service negotiations
  considerations 56
  key considerations 50
fee-for-value 5
fee schedules
  key atrributes 46
financial considerations
  bundled payments 92
financial responsibility matrix
  capitation/global payments 128
financial rewards
  capitation/global payments 126
  shared savings/risk 102
financial scenario implications
  capitation/global payments 134
financial scenarios
  evaulating 76
full risk 117. *See also* global capitation
fundamental drivers 89
  capitation/global payments 123
  list 89
  shared savings/risk 101
fund distribution 120
  capitation/global payments 139
funds distribution
  capitation/global payments 120

G

geographic practice cost indexes (GPCIs) 44
global capitation
  full risk. *See also* global capitation
global payment 115. *See* capitation
goals/objectives
  focus on 72

H

healthcare spending
  government projections 2
Health Maintenance Organizations (HMOs) 15
Health Policy Research Group, University of Oregon 33
HEDIS
  measures list 36
  quality metrics 36
Hibbard, Judith DPH 33
hierarchical condition category (HCC) 124
high-deductible plans 18
high-level fee-for-service analysis 54
high-level steps 144
high-value choices
  making, study 33
Hospital Compare and Physician Compare 32

I

identifying essential questions
  value proposition 151
increasing quality 101
incurred but not reported (IBNR) 121
initial proposal 155
  grid 156
innovation models 84
  bundled payments 84
Institute for Healthcare Improvement's Triple Aim 5

K

key attributes
  added-payment methodologies 65
  bundled payments 87
  capitation/global payment 116
  fee schedules 46
  increases reimbursement 65
  P4P reimbursement contracts 65
  shared savings risk 99
key considerations
  fee-for-service negotiations 50
  negotiations, pay for performance 73
key drivers
  P4P contracts 68
key focus
  advancing care information 62
  clinical practice improvement 62

cost 61
quality 61

L

limiting risk 99
  capitation/global payment 118

M

MACRA 39, 60, 63
malpractice RVU 44
Managed Care Contracting Continuum 39, 153
Managed Care Organizations (MCOs) 46
management cost
  expenses 56
market/payer assessment 152
Medical Loss Ratio (MLR) 153
medical PFS payments rates formula 44
Medicare
  Quality Payment Program 3
Medicare Access and CHIP Reauthorization Act (MACRA) 3
Medicare payer category 64
Medicare Physician Fee Schedule 85
  fee-for-service method 44
  (PFS) (Part B) 44
Medicare Quality Payment Program
  dvanced Alternative Payment Model (APM) 3
  Merit-Based Incentive Payment System (MIPS) 3
Medicare Shared Savings Program (MSSP) 4
  ACOs 63
Medicare Sustainable Growth Rate (SGR) 60
member months 119
  capitation/global payments 119
MIPS 60
mission statement 147
monitor contract performance 159
monitoring denials 161
monitoring payer website 160
MSSP Tracks 2 & 3 and Next Generation ACO 64

N

narrow networks 15, 40, 72
narrow networks negative cost containing
  factors 17
narrow provider network
  clinically integrated 16
  employer specific 16

high performance 16
high value 16
sub network 16
tailored 16
tiered 16
National Quality Forum (NQF)
  quality metrics 36
negotiation considerations
  bundled payments 90, 93
  capitation/global payments 127
  shared savings/risk 103
negotiations, pay for performance
  key considerations 73
new reimbursement models
  medicare and medicaid 39
Next Generation ACO 4

O

Oncology Care Model Two-Sided Risk Arrangement 4
  (OCM) 64
OptumInsight
  (Ingenix) 45
Outcome Incentive Award program (OIA) 60

P

P4P sample matrix 70
Patient Centered Medical Home accreditation 33
Patient Centered Medical Homes (PCMH) 64
Patient-Centered Outcomes Research Institute (PCORI)
  quality metrics 36
patient liability
  impact of manged-care contracts 27
  increasing 40
patients
  raw risk score 124
Payer Assessment 153
Payer proprietary fee schedules
  fee-for-service method 44
payer website 150
pay-for-performance
  ER visit estimated savings 77
  (P4P) 7, 59
  practice performance comparison 78
  progress chart 77
  sample contract math 79
payment/fee schedules

    algorithms 44
payment negotiations
    key considerations 50
PCMH Program Performance Report 140
per member per month (PMPM) 116
Physician Compare website 32
plurality 104
plurality of care
    capitation/global payments 132
PMPM 120
PMPM calculation 104
population health management 123
PPO 72
practice 'add-ons' 146
practice expense RVU 44
Preferred Provider Organizations (PPOs) 15
private exchanges
    insurance 22
    multi-carrier exchanges 23
    single-carrier exchanges 23
provider defined network 24

Q

Quality and Resource Use Reports (QRURs) 32, 67, 149
quality measures
    outcome 36
    patient experience 36
    process 35
    structure 35
quality metrics 40, 68, 72, 105
    Agency for Healthcare Research and Quality (AHRQ) 36
    Consumer Assessment of Healthcare Providers and Systems (CAHPS) 36
    HEDIS 36
    National Quality Forum (NQF) 36
    Patient-Centered Outcomes Research Institute (PCORI) 36
Quality Payment Program models
    CJR and Cardiac Demonstration (risk dependent) 4
    Comprehensive Primary Care Plus (CPC+) 4
    Comprenehsive ESRD Care (CEC) 4
    Medicare Shared Savings Program (MSSP) 4
    Next Generation ACO 4
    Oncology Care Model Two-Sided Risk Arrangement 4
quality performance measures 66
    cost efficiency 66
quick reference guide
    necessity of 159

R

Rand Corporation, the 27
raw risk score 124
RBRVS 44
reimbursement methodology 59
Reinsurance or stop-loss insurance 135
review information 67
risk categories
  capitation/global payment 117
risk pools 120
  capitation/global risk 119
risk stratification 123, 124
  categorizing patients 124
  constellation of morbidities 125
RVU 44

S

sample contract monitoring grid 161
sample matrix
  P4P 70
samples
  diagnostic test time for interpretation of a stroke 149
  facility utilization comparison 149
  well visit comparison 148
severity adjust 19
shared-risk program 60
shared savings/risk 7, 97
  attribution methodology 104
  financial rewards 102
  financial scenario implications 106
  fundamental drivers 101
  key attributes 99
  negotiation considerations 103
  plurality 104
  risk-based reimbursement methodology 97
  scope of services 104
shared savings/risk examples 108
shared savings/risk negotiation check lis 111
system fragmentation 17

T

The Managed Care Contracting Continuum 7
transparency 31, 40
transparency tools 32
  to manage waste 32

Triple Aim 5, 11, 27, 40, 59, 150
  objects of 11
Triple Aim Test 13
trueing up
  bundled payments 83
types of APMs
  bundled payments programs 63
  CMS innovation center initiatives 64
  comprehensive ESRD care (CEC) model 64
  comprehensive primary care plus (CPC+) 64
  medicare shared savings program (MSSP) ACOs 63
  MSSP tracks 2 & 3 and next generation ACO 64
  oncology care model two-sided risk arrangement (OCM) 64
  patient centered medical homes (PCMH) 64

U

Usual and customary rates
  fee-for-service method 44
Usual, Customary and Reasonable (UCR) 45

V

value-based
  payment environment 18
value-based contracting 40
value-driven arrangements 72
value proposition 1, 143
  construction of a practice's 34
  differentiate 146
  identifying essential questions 151
  mission statement 147
  outcomes and sources 148
value proposition chart 145
virtual bundle
  bundled payments 83

W

withholds 119
  capitation/global payments 119
Workers' Compensation fee schedules
  fee-for-service method 44
work RVU 44

CPSIA information can be obtained
at www.ICGtesting.com
Printed in the USA
LVOW03s1927201016
509505LV00001B/1/P